Highlights
Creative Craft
Activities

Edited by Caroline Clark Myers

Foreword

From the wealth of materials published in earlier issues of HIGHLIGHTS FOR CHILDREN, we have selected and adapted those features which seem to have the greatest merit in the light of our experiences in the schoolroom, and from our observation of teachers and children. This handbook presents suggestions for creative projects for the leading holidays and seasons of the school year.

—*The Editors*, HIGHLIGHTS FOR CHILDREN

Library of Congress Catalog Card Number: 67-28201.

Copyright © 1967, by HIGHLIGHTS FOR CHILDREN, Inc. Columbus, Ohio. All rights reserved.

ISBN 0-87534-554-9

Paper Cup Fun

By Marjorie Weed

A package of pointed paper cups will last a long time and will make a variety of things. Use them for clown hats, Indian tepees, or heads of bugs. Make them into flowers by pasting, inside the lip, a strip of paper that has been fringed, scalloped, or cut to points. They are perfect for bodies with lollipops for heads. Decorate them with crayons. Use a strong glue to paste on tissue-paper fringe, buttons, bits of yarn, and the like.

A few suggestions are pictured. Your fun will be in working out your own creations, using materials you have on hand.

Halloween Craft

A Sitting Pumpkin

By Lee Lindeman

Trim off a small amount from the bottom of a small pumpkin and from the top of a larger pumpkin. Place the small pumpkin on top of the larger one, flat top to flat bottom. The pumpkin should now fit steadily together.

The legs and arms can be made from pencils pushed into the pumpkin. Hands and feet can be made from paper and pasted to the eraser end of the pencils. Clay can also be used to make the hands and feet.

You are ready to decorate your sitting pumpkin. A marking pen, poster paint, vegetables, and candy can be used for putting on the details. For example, the greens of a carrot can be put on with toothpicks for hair or even a beard. Half of an olive would be wonderful for an eye. The eyebrows, mouth, and freckles can be put on with paint or a marking pen.

What would you use for ears? A slice of potato? Many of the details can be made from curled paper, gumdrops, and cotton.

Have fun creating a fantastic Halloween pumpkin person.

Witch Decoration

By Beatrice Bachrach

These Halloween witches make good three-dimensional wall and door decorations. Cut a head shape from orange construction paper. Cut long black paper strips (or strands of black yarn). Glue them to both sides of the head for hair. Cut out and paste on a pointed black hat. Cut an orange triangle for a projecting nose. Fold down about ½ to ¾ inch at the wide end, and paste the folded part to the face.

Place Cards

By Lee Lindeman

Parties are more fun when you have place cards. A black cat, a scary witch, or a funny pumpkin face on a place card are all easy to make.

Ask your grocer, when he is unpacking layers of fruit, to save you one of the fruit separators. Cut out the cup-shaped dents in it to use for heads.

Trim the edge of each cup shape evenly. Glue it to a heavy piece of paper. Trim off all the extra paper except what you need for ears, stem, or hat. Paint the head with poster paint. Add details with a small brush.

The place card is a square of heavy paper folded in half. Glue the character head to it as shown. Print the name on the paper.

Make many of these—each different—for your party at school or at home.

Pumpkin Heads

By Ella L. Langenberg

Make a ball of cotton large enough to fill the hand. Place it in the center of a square of crepe paper or a paper napkin. Round off the corners. Leave enough paper around the ball to pull up and cover the cotton.

Remove the cotton and turn the paper over. Draw a face with crayon. Hold it firmly so it does not tear. Put the cotton back on the paper and gather the paper at the top of the head. Tie it with string or thread.

Make several heads. Tie them to string or wire as shown. Tie bows on each pumpkin head.

Push two sticks down into a box of sand or soil, far enough so they will stand up. Cover the box with paper, or paint it with tempera paint. Suspend the string of pumpkin heads between the sticks.

Cornhusk Characters

By Katherine Corliss Bartow

For each doll select eight soft inner cornhusks about 8 inches long and an inch wide. Dampen them and lay them one on top of the other.

Fold the pile in half. Tie off a head at the folded end with thread. Insert three small pieces of husk under the head for arms. Tie at the waistline and at the wrists. For legs, separate the husks and tie at the ankles. Cut off all ends evenly. Use colored paper or ink for features, and husks for hair.

Now create your own characters, using felt or crepe paper for trim, front and back. Illustrated are Red Riding Hood, a clown, and a scarecrow.

Hang them by threads for a mobile or decoration. Or glue the feet to cards for party place card favors.

Noisy Jumping Spiders and Bugs

By Lee Lindeman

Why don't you try creating a few fantastic spiders and bugs? These creatures can really jump.

Get a fruit separator from your grocer. Cut out the cupshaped dents. Place a few dried beans or corn kernels in each cup shape, and glue a heavy piece of paper over it. Trim when the glue is dry.

Paint the body with tempera or poster paint. Add other details with paint or colored paper. Paste legs to the underside of the body. They can be made from pipe cleaners or heavy paper strips, with colored-paper feet pasted on the ends.

Glue a long piece of elastic thread or a rubber band to the top. Tie a button or curtain ring to the other end to help keep it in your hand as you make the bug jump.

Owl Mask

By Ruth Libbey

Use a heavy brown-paper bag or a large envelope. Hold it up to the face, and figure out where the eyes should be. Cut out two big round eyeholes, and a diamond-shaped hole for the nose as shown. Cut out the mask, leaving enough paper to cover the face and to make owl ears at the top.

Make a feather pattern on cardboard, and trace around it on brown paper. Several may be made at a time. Color them with brown crayon. Using paste on one end only, attach the feathers to the lower part of the mask.

For the beak, cut a piece of paper about 2 inches square. Fold it from corner to corner. Cut along the fold about a half inch at one end. Poke it through the nose opening and tape in place.

Glue a strip of colored cellophane across the eye openings on the back. A piece of heavy paper may be glued along the edges on the wrong side to hold the cellophane in place.

Punch a hole at each side of the mask. Tie a piece of ribbon or yarn in each hole, then tie to one or two rubber bands looped together. The mask will easily slip on and off.

A Funny Pumpkin Card

By Ruth Libbey

Fold a piece of heavy orange construction paper in half for the card. Draw a 5-inch circle on it as shown, and cut it out to the folded edge only. This fold forms the hinge for the double pumpkin card.

Draw eyes, nose, and mouth on the outside pumpkin and cut them out. Trace around these cutout spaces onto the other pumpkin. With black crayon write BOO! BOO! with the first O of each BOO in the middle of each eye. Over the mouth write a word like HELLO! The black lettering will look like funny teeth.

A Stand-up Witch

By Lucile Rosencrans

Cut a triangle from heavy paper. Color or paint a face near the top, leaving the point of the triangle for the top of the hat. Color hair and clothes.

A strip of paper makes the arms and hands. Color both sides. Fold the witch in half, and cut slits just below the face. Run the arms through the slits.

Cut out and color an oval-shaped hat brim. Make a slit in the center to fit over the head. Bend the arms slightly forward, and spread the triangle so the witch will stand. Use for a Halloween decoration.

Black Bat Family

By Ruth Dougherty

These bats are made from black construction paper with scraps of orange paper or glowing tape for eyes. The patterns shown give dimensions for the medium-size bat. For smaller and larger bats, simply cut the circles and wings about an inch smaller or larger. Cut on the solid lines of the pattern, and fold on the dotted lines.

Roll the body half-circle into a cone, slightly open at the pointed end. Paste it along the overlapping edge.

When cutting the head pattern, be sure to include the two points for the ears. Cut out and paste the eyes in place. Then roll the half-circle into a very pointed cone, and paste.

Fasten the head to the pointed end of the body with a small strip of black paper, one end under the chin, the other inside the cone to the lower part of the body.

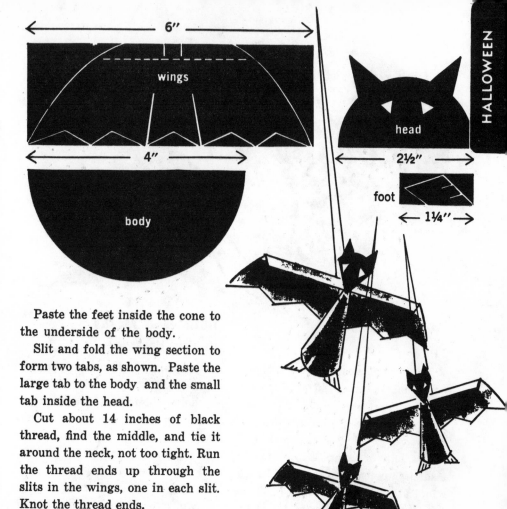

Paste the feet inside the cone to the underside of the body.

Slit and fold the wing section to form two tabs, as shown. Paste the large tab to the body and the small tab inside the head.

Cut about 14 inches of black thread, find the middle, and tie it around the neck, not too tight. Run the thread ends up through the slits in the wings, one in each slit. Knot the thread ends.

When hung on a curtain or hook, the bat will seem to be flying.

Katcina Mask

By Dale M. Everson

Slip a large flat-bottomed paper bag over the head. Have someone mark the places where the eyeholes should be.

Remove the bag and cut out the holes. Paste strips of colored paper around the holes for trim.

Cut a sheet of construction paper in half. Roll one half into a tube shape for a nose. Paste or tape it together. Cut slits around one end of the tube, and press out the little flaps. Paste the tube nose to the bag by these flaps.

Use scraps of colored paper to cut out Indian designs. Paste them across the bottom and on the cheeks of the mask.

Cut the remaining half of the construction-paper sheet in two for ears. Paste Indian designs on each piece. Fold back an inch on each ear to form an edge to paste to the bag.

Use two sheets of colored construction paper for feathers. Fold, and cut them in half, the long way. Trim the top to a point. Slash along the long edges. Fold up 2 inches at the bottom and attach to the mask.

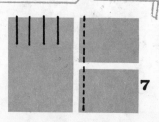

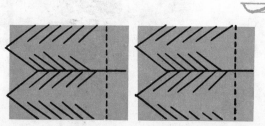

7

Witch Hazel
By Barbara Baker

Make this witch from construction paper triangles of different sizes and colors, some with jagged edges and some with smooth. Cut holes in the dress or paste on patches.

Now use your imagination and see what kind of witch you can make.

Paper Mosaic
By D. P. Barnhouse

Paper mosaics make colorful and unusual pictures. Sketch a master design in colored chalk on a piece of cardboard. From construction paper, cut out ½-inch squares of a variety of colors. Also cut odd shapes to use where your design indicates, such as triangular pieces for ears. Keep pieces of the same color together in separate boxes.

Using rubber cement, glue, or paste, fill in the design with the paper tiles. A little background color showing between each tile gives the mosaic its distinctive character.

Give the completed picture a coat of varnish to protect the surface and give it the shiny look of real tile.

Halloween Masks
By Fran Harvey

Put a brown paper bag over your head and mark the place for the eyeholes. Remove the bag and cut out the holes. Draw the cat's eyes, nose, and mouth as shown. Color the mask as desired.

Fold a sheet of black construction paper and cut two ears as shown, leaving them connected at the fold. Glue or tape them to the top of the bag. Add some broom straws for whiskers.

An elephant and a pirate are also shown, but you will probably prefer to design your own mask.

Soda Straw Scarecrow
By Agnes Choate Wonson

Form the scarecrow on a planter stick such as florists use. The materials needed are three colored soda straws, felt or oilcloth for coat and hat, a marshmallow for the face, and cloves for eyes and mouth.

Cut 4 inches off each straw. Use the short ends for the arms. Fasten them crosswise to the 4-inch straws with string or rubber bands. Glue this to the planter stick, 1½ inches from the pointed end.

Cut the coat shape on a fold of felt or oilcloth. Slit a neck opening at the fold. Slip it over the top of the stick and glue in place. For the face, press a small marshmallow flat, push in cloves for features, and glue to the stick. Cut and glue on the hat. Add felt or painted-on buttons.

Play Mask

By M. Mable Lunz

Cut the mask from lightweight cardboard or construction paper. Make a bow from colored ribbon and staple it to the top at one side. On the opposite side attach an unsharpened pencil or a piece of smooth wood at the back of the mask. Roll in the sides of the mask a little but do not fold. The mask may be crayoned or painted or trimmed with sequins, beads, or silver paper.

If used as a party favor, stick it into a cupcake or candy bar, with the guest's name on the mask.

A Ghost

By Martha Carpenter

Make ghosts to decorate your room, using marshmallows and stiff white paper napkins.

With a toothpick and melted chocolate, draw eyes, nose, and mouth on the marshmallow. Pick up the napkin at the center, round off the corners with scissors, and spread for the dress. Push a short stick through the napkin center, then into the marshmallow head.

Clown Fun

By Vinetta Kendrick

Fans. For Figure 1, make pattern A. Start with a 6½-inch circle, add pointed neck ruff and cap, and cut out the shape. Using this pattern, cut out two shapes, one from heavy colored construction paper and one from white. The handle is cut from heavy white cardboard.

On the white shape, draw the clown's face and cap lightly in pencil. Glue on button eyes. Crayon the face, cap, and ruff, using bright colors. Glue the two shapes together at the cap and at the center and bottom of the face, inserting the handle at the bottom.

The smaller fan, Figure 2, is made in the same way, using pattern B which starts with a 4½-inch circle. The handle is a crayoned tongue depressor. For the eyes, use glitter sprinkled on glue.

Pictures. The round picture, Figure 3, is a 9-inch circle of white paper with a 9-inch hanger doubled into a loop and stapled or pasted at the top. For the clown, use pattern B.

Figure 4 is made on a 9-by-12-inch cardboard covered with colored felt and framed with gummed tape. For the clown, use pattern B. Pencil on the pattern sections to be in color, and cut the pattern apart. Use these parts to cut the sections from different colors of felt. Paste them in place. Add other decorations as desired. The sample shown has colored sequins, stars, and pieces of pine cone.

Fig.1

Fig.2

Fig.3

Fig.4

A

B

Come-alive Box

By Lee Lindeman

An animal can be made from a box of almost any size. Use the box for the body. Glue on legs made from heavy paper or cardboard. The neck can be an empty tissue roll or a paper roll that you've made yourself. Tape or glue the neck to the body. Draw an animal head on heavy paper, cut it out, and glue it to the neck. You will have fun painting it with bright colors.

9

Bagged Indians

By Beatrice Bachrach

Fill a bag about three quarters full of crumpled newspaper. Paste or tape the bag closed. On one side paint or draw facial features, adding war paint. Fit a long piece of black paper on each side of the head for hair. Fringe it, and paste or tape in place. Cut a headband. Paste paper feathers along the inside of the band. Poke a hole in the bottom of the head. Push a broom handle up into this hole. You now have an unusual dance partner.

Halloween Cat

By Ruth Everding Libbey

Two cups, cut from an egg carton, make this little cat. Try to cut one cup so that it has corners on it to resemble ears; otherwise, glue on ears cut from black paper. Outline eyes and nose with black crayon. Inside the outline, color the eyes and nose orange.

Color the two cups black with paint or crayon. Glue them together. When dry, place the cat on its back and put a drop of glue on the nose. Stick three tiny broom straws in the glue for whiskers. Heavy black thread will also do for whiskers. This cat will make a nice party favor.

Owl Mask

By Catherine Urban

Use a heavy brown paper bag, the kind that folds flat. Be sure it is large enough to fit your head. Spread out the sides, then bend down the corners. Sew across them carefully. These form the owl's ears.

Put the bag over the head and place a mark at the eyes. Draw a pointed nose with red crayon. Cut two large circles of white paper and two smaller ones of black. Paste the white ones over the eye marks, then paste the black ones over the white. Cut slits in the eyes to see through the mask, and a slash below the nose to breathe through. Cut the bottom of the bag in jagged points.

Put on the mask, tie loosely around the neck, and let the points stick out like a ruff.

Small bags may be made into place cards or favors. Place a popcorn ball wrapped in wax paper inside the bag. Tie with ribbon. Then spread out the ruff and paste it to a yellow card. Write the name of the guest on the card.

Balloon Jack-o'-lantern

By Viora Scott

Blow up a balloon as large as the pumpkin is to be. Tie the neck tightly. Wind a string several times around the balloon from top to bottom, leaving a space between each wind. Draw the string very tight so it pinches into the balloon to make the ridges on the pumpkin. Tie the string.

Pour a large bottle of cellulose glue into an old dish, or use flour and water paste. Tear orange crepe paper into strips long enough to go around the balloon. Wet a strip in the glue. Working quickly so it will not dry, lay the strip loosely around the balloon. Keep it round on the top and flat on the bottom. This is easy to do by starting each strip on the bottom and overlapping the ends. Set the balloon down each time a strip is put on and it will flatten itself. The crepe paper should be quite wet.

Be careful to let the paper strips settle into the ridges. Do not draw it too tight. And don't worry if it seems a bit uneven—pumpkins are naturally that way. Put on at least three coats of crepe paper. Do not allow it to dry between coats.

The neck of the balloon will be the stem. Cover it with green paper.

Set the finished pumpkin on a heavy piece of cardboard for a base. Let it dry overnight. With a sharp knife, cut off the lid and cut out the facial features.

Do NOT use a lighted candle in this pumpkin.

Decorative Masks

By Frances M. Callahan

These masks are for decorative purposes. They can be used for party decorations or around the front door to greet your friends when they come to your home for trick or treat. Two, stapled together back to back, may be hung from a doorway as a mobile, or they may be hung on the wall.

Use the back of an aluminum "TV dinner" tray for the front of the mask. Paint it if desired.

For face features, use scrap materials such as buttons, bottle caps, felt, construction paper, and pipe cleaners. Hair can be made from untwisted twine, rope, yarn, or paper ribbon. Attach all decorations with white glue.

Halloween Window Rattler By Lee Lindeman

This is a new kind of Halloween window rattler. You will need a long, strong stick or branch, a cardboard fruit or vegetable tray, some small stones or beans, cardboard, and colored construction paper.

Cut a small notch at each end of the tray. Place one end of the stick along the tray, fitting it into the notches. Glue in place.

Place the beans or stones in the tray. Glue a piece of cardboard over the whole tray to hold the beans or stones inside. Trim off any excess. Paint the tray any desired color.

Cut a cat's face, a pumpkin face, or even a witch's face from construction paper. The face should be larger than the tray. Glue the face to the tray. Decorate in any way you wish.

You are now ready for Halloween. Hold the rattler in front of a window and shake it.

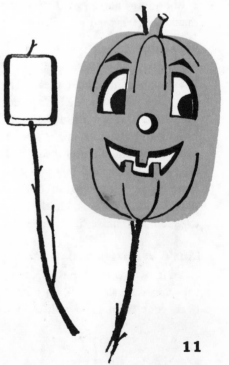

Masks

By Lee Lindeman

It is fun to make your own mask to wear with your Halloween costume. Here are four basic suggestions for masks you can make.

Use your imagination for design and trim. Yarn or curled paper makes wonderful hair. So does cotton or old fur. Pipe cleaners make good whiskers or feelers. Sequins or glitter add glamour. A standout nose and odd-shaped ears change the whole character of the mask.

Shoelaces make good ties for masks that have to be tied on.

Binocular Mask

Hold a 4-by-12-inch piece of heavy paper up to your face. Mark the place for the eyeholes and cut them out. Cut a toilet tissue tube in half and glue one half over each eyehole. When the glue has dried, shape the mask and paint it with tempera or poster paint. Colored paper was used to trim the tube eyes on the mask illustrated.

Mask With Human Ears

Your own ears will stick out of this paper mask which slips down over your head. You will need a piece of heavy colored construction paper 24 inches long and 9 inches wide. Place the paper over your face and mark with crayon or chalk where the eyes, nose, mouth, and ears should be.

Before you cut, let a friend check to see if the marks are in the right places, and to mark where the mask should overlap at the back for a snug fit.

Cut out the eyes, ears, mouth, and part of the nose as shown. Be sure that the earholes are large enough for your ears to go through. Decorate as desired. Fasten the mask together at the back with glue or staples.

Paper Tray Mask

Use a molded paper tray that your mother gets at the store. Clean the tray with a damp sponge and let it dry thoroughly. Hold the tray up to your face and mark the place for the eyes and nose. Carefully cut small holes for the eyes and a larger hole for the nose. Paint the mask with tempera paint, using different colors and shapes to bring out the features. The pointed ears shown are from heavy paper, and the feelers are pipe cleaners.

Eye Mask

Get a fruit separator from your grocer. Cut out two of the cup-shaped dents. Trim them carefully. Cut a hole the size of a quarter in the center of each cup shape.

Cut a piece of heavy paper 4 by 12 inches. Hold it up to your face to see where your eyes would come on the paper. Cut holes the size of a quarter where the eyes should be. Now glue the cups to the heavy paper over the eyeholes.

When the glue has dried, cut the mask to the desired shape and paint with tempera or poster paint.

Pumpkin Heads

By Jean Hale

These personality pumpkin heads are a far cry from the old-fashioned jack-o'-lantern. The pumpkin you select may be round or oblong. Place it on a cardboard ring to keep it from rolling and also to provide a neck for the head.

Dapper Dan. The hair, eyebrows, and mustache are made of cotton, held in place with pins. Hollow out two eyeholes in the pumpkin and insert ping pong balls so they are about half hidden. Paint the eyes with blue poster paint. Paint the eye centers black. Leave a pie-shaped part of the eye unpainted as illustrated. It will make the eyes shine. The nose is a red apple fastened in place with a lollipop stick. Add construction paper ears and a gay scarf.

Sweet Sue. Scouring pads, the kind that can be stretched, make hair of shining gold. They are held in place with pins. The eyes are arcs of black paper, fringed with scissors. The eyebrows are painted on with poster paint. The turned-up nose is the end of a yellow pepper, anchored with pins. For the lips, cut a hole in the pumpkin and push a small red apple in until about half of it is showing. A little poster paint for rouge, a crepe paper collar, and a bow for the hair are the finishing touches.

Otto Out. This character has a green cucumber nose pushed into a hole in the center of the face. The eyes are marshmallows, painted with blue and black poster paint. Pins will hold them on. Cut the big teeth out of cardboard and paste them to a thin strip of black paper. Pin this in place. Cut the ears from any bright construction paper. Make them very large. The shaggy hair is celery tops.

Wicked Witch. No Halloween party would be complete without a wicked witch. Remove the pulp from the pumpkin. Make the hole at the pumpkin top fairly large. Cut holes for the eyes and fasten pieces of orange paper over them inside the pumpkin. Paint a black dot in the center of each eye.

Replace the pumpkin lid. Make the hat of black construction paper. Use strips of black construction paper for the hair. Pin the strips to the head before putting on the hat. The nose is a curving pepper. The teeth can be as jagged as your knife will make them. If you put the witch on a small table, you can make her black crepe paper cape long enough to cover the entire table.

Let your imagination take over as you dream up more pumpkin heads for your Halloween party.

Owl Bookmark

By Agnes Choate Wonson

Cut the long tab from thin sponge rubber such as comes on cleaners' coat hangers. Cut the owl head from black felt. Add notebook reinforcement rings for eyes, or cut them from white paper. Paste the head to the tab with the bottom free so it will slide over a page top.

Paper-Bag Turkey

By Lucile Rosencrans

Use a brown paper bag, any size. Fill the lower half loosely with crushed newspaper, and tie the bag closed with string. Cut down one side of the bag opening as far as the string. Lay the bag on its side. The bottom of it will be the front of the turkey. Spread open end of the bag out in a fan shape and cup it forward to make the tail. Decorate the turkey with water colors or crayons.

Draw and cut out a head the right size for the body. Paint it like the body, adding a red wattle and an orange bill. Paste it to the front of the turkey.

Set the turkey on a table or pin it to the wall for decoration.

Paper-Bag Owl Family

By Ruth Dougherty

These owls are made from brown-paper grocery bags with square bottoms — large, medium, and small size. Press the bag flat, with sides poked in and bottom brought forward, following the creases.

The bag bottom is the owl's face. Staple the lower corners to the side of the bag as shown. With black crayon, draw streaks and half-circles over the entire front and back, for feathers.

Ears, beak, and eyes are orange construction paper, with white eye centers. Paste the eyes in place with just a dab of glue so the outside edges will stand out. Paste the top of the beak to the bag bottom only, so the point will stand out.

Stuff the bag with shredded newspaper till it is nice and plump. Then slit the bag opening 2 or 3 inches up the center, and tie off each side to form feet as shown.

Make a string loop hanger and tape it to the back of the owl.

Funny Clown Party Favor

By Ruth Everding Libbey

Cut out four cups from a cardboard egg carton. Glue two of them together to make the head. Paint on eyes, nose, and mouth.

Color two more cups for the body and hat.

Cut out three or four circles from a paper napkin, tracing around a glass to get the circle shape. Cut scallops around the edges. Glue them, one by one, to the top of the body cup, then add the head. On top of the head, glue the hat cup. Tape a toothpaste tube cap to the top of the hat.

Owl Mosaic   By Joy N. Hulme

For the background use 9-by-12 inch cardboard or corrugated paper. Draw on it the outline of an owl. Bend and cut white pipe cleaners to fit these pencil lines. Paste the pipe cleaner pieces in place.

The tail is real feathers. The rest of the owl is covered with dried berries, melon seeds, and the like. Perhaps Mother will find some things in the kitchen that you could use, such as dried split peas and peppers and whole spices.

Place these around on the owl and perch to decide where to use them. Then paste them in place, spreading glue over one area at a time. Place a row around the inside of the pipe cleaner, then fill in the center, pressing the pieces close together as you work.

When the picture is completed, cover it with an old magazine and weight it down with a heavy book till the paste dries.

Bobbing Characters   By Phyllis Fanders

Silly characters can be made from discarded jar rubbers, and odds and ends.

Start with two rubbers. Place glue around the edge of one, and lay a piece of plastic wrap or cellophane over it. The character illustrated has notebook reinforcement circles for eyes, yarn nose, mouth, hair, and beard, and paper ears decorated on both sides.

When all the features are pasted in place, cover the face with another piece of cellophane, then glue the second rubber to it. Run a rubber band through the top of the rubbers for a hanger.

With this as a starter, see what silly characters you can create from the odds and ends you have on hand.

Colonial Doll   By Dorothe A. Palms

For the skirt, use seven cone-shaped paper cups. Insert a 5-inch pipe cleaner through the point of each cup, looping the end to keep it from sliding through. Twist the pipe cleaners together to join the cups into a full skirt.

Cut several 3½-inch circles from colored material and net, or construction paper and greeting cards. Punch a small hole at the centers, and push the circles down over the pipe cleaners.

For the blouse, cut a cup down to 3½ inches, snip off the point, and push it down over the pipe cleaners, with the wide part at the top for the shoulders. Flatten it and cut slits down each crease.

Lay a 10-inch pipe cleaner inside, fitting it into the slits for arms.

To a foam-ball head add paper features and cotton hair. Push a 5-inch pipe cleaner into the ball about 1½ inches. Make the collar from ovals of the same material as the skirt. Push the rest of the pipe cleaner through the collar and down into the blouse. Glue the blouse completely flat.

For sleeves, push each pipe-cleaner arm through a 2-inch point from a paper cup.

Cut a fan-shaped bonnet from an old greeting card and pleat it. Glue to the back of the head.

Add ribbon bows at the bonnet back, neck, and waist.

Decorate the skirt, blouse, sleeves, and bonnet with glitter or flowers cut from greeting cards.

Staple or glue the skirt cups together so the doll will stand.

Paper Plate Turkey   By Gladys Emerson

Paint the bottom of a 9- or 10-inch paper plate with brown tempera or water color. Cut it in half and place together, face to face. From scraps of colored construction paper cut six or eight long, pointed feathers for the tail. Insert these between the paper plates. Cut four or five smaller feathers and glue on each side for the wings. From brown construction paper, cut a head. Make beak and eyes from small scraps of construction paper. Insert head between paper plates. Glue all of this in place by putting glue around the rim of the plates and pressing them together. These make nice centerpieces for a Thanksgiving dinner table.

Easy-to-make Bookmark

By Texie Hering

The base for this bookmark is a metal hair clip similar to the one shown. Glue a colored construction paper covering on the inside of each prong—the same shape but a little larger. This extra paper gives something to which the shapes may be glued.

Any desired shapes for the front and back may be cut from colored felt or heavy construction paper. Notice in the illustrations how the back shape completes the front shape. Features and other lines are drawn on with black or white ink.

Pilgrim Bonnet

By Ouida A. Moore

To make this Pilgrim bonnet, use a man's discarded white shirt with a starched collar. Put the collar around your face for the brim of the bonnet. Pull the rest of the shirt back like a ponytail.

Tie securely with a white string or ribbon, or a strip cut from the facing of the shirt. Cut off the shirt about 3 or 4 inches below the knot. Your bonnet is finished and ready to wear.

Twirly Tops

By Ruth Libbey

These tops are made from food container lids of metal or plastic. Cut out a circle of colored paper to fit the top. Glue in place. Then cut out a smaller round piece of a different colored paper. Fold it two or three times and cut in a fancy design. Open it out and glue it to the lid. Other ideas for decorations are shown.

Carefully hammer a shingle nail (about an inch long with a large flat head) in the center of each top. Be sure to place a piece of wood under it when you hammer the nail. Hammer it in just a little way. Glue a piece of colored paper to the nailhead to make the top more colorful. Use the nailhead to spin the top.

These would be fun to make at a party, and give prizes for the prettiest one or the one that spins the longest.

Tommy Cat
By Luella Pierce

Fold 9-by-12-inch yellow construction paper to 6-by-9 size. Draw the body with the neck on the fold. Cut it out, leaving the folded edge at the neck uncut. Draw feet and other lines with black crayon.

Cut the head from black paper, 5 by 5 inches. Outline the eyes, nose, mouth, and whiskers with white crayon. Fasten the head to the body with a two-prong fastener so the head will tilt from side to side.

Cut the tail from black paper. Make a 1-inch slit in the center of the large end. Fold the two parts in opposite directions to make tabs for pasting to the cat's back as shown in the illustration.

Spread the feet so the cat will stand.

Tube Tricks
By Lee Lindeman

Make a napkin ring, comb holder, pencil holder, and even a bobby-pin holder from the cardboard tube in waxed paper or paper towels.

The pencil holder will need a firm base made of heavy cardboard cut slightly larger than the end of a 4-inch-long tube. Glue one end of the tube to the base.

After the glue has dried, paint the holder. Add designs with paint or paper. This can also be used as a comb holder.

Attractive napkin rings can be made by cutting off 1-inch rings from a tube. Paint each ring a solid color, and decorate with a name or a design such as flowers, fish, or an abstraction.

For a bobby-pin holder, carefully cut a 1½-inch ring from a cardboard tube. Glue to a heavy cardboard base that has been cut slightly larger than the ring. Paint the holder inside and out. After the paint is dry, decorate with lace or sequins, or cover with paper you have designed.

Plastic Container With Weaving
By Ruth Dougherty

This container may be small enough to hold a water glass for flowers or ivy, or large enough to hold a flowerpot.

Use an empty plastic container such as detergent or bleach comes in. Cut off the top of the container at the desired height. You might scallop the top edge of a plain container. A pencil line helps guide the cutting.

Cut an even number of vertical slits around the middle of the container as shown. These may range from an inch or two to the full length, according to how much weaving is desired.

The weaving strips are cut from the top of the container which was cut off. Cut narrow strips for small containers, wider for larger containers. Cut each strip an inch longer than the span around the container and overlap to hold in place after weaving. Or one long continuous strip may be used, overlapping when a new one needs to be joined. These strips may be painted with enamel or nail polish, if desired.

Weave colored plastic lacing between the strips. Allow enough to tie into a bow.

The possibilities of designs and variety are many. Try your own.

Dancing Clown

By Catherine Corliss Bartow

For the body, wrap a 16-by-4-inch piece of colored crepe paper around a dowel, and glue. When dry, crush the paper by pushing the ends toward the center of the dowel. Remove the crepe paper.

Repeat with crepe paper 7 by 4 inches for arms, and 8 by 4 inches for legs.

Fold over and glue the paper at all openings except the neck. Glue the legs and arms in place.

Cut two 2½-inch circles from heavy white construction paper. Glue them together with a half inch of the clown's neck inserted between them.

For the hat, cut a 2¼-inch triangle from a colored envelope corner, or color a white one. Slit the

sides a half inch and turn up for a brim. Make a pompon from 4-by-1-inch crepe paper fringed with ¾-inch slits. Glue it to the point of the hat. Turn the fringe down.

Use black paper for eyes and nose, and red paper for the mouth. Glue four ¾-inch strands of brown yarn hair to each side of the head, front and back. Glue the hat in place, with a loop of cord inserted at the back.

For the ruff, gather a 7-by-1½-inch length of crepe paper. Glue it around the neck. Add colored paper circles for buttons.

Hold the cord and shake the clown sidewise gently to make it twist and sway.

This clown also makes a colorful room decoration.

Envelope Bookmark Gift

By Lola J. Janes

Cut off the corner of a white or colored envelope, then cut off the closed corner of the piece as shown. The edges may be cut with pinking shears or cut straight or with a slight curve.

With colored ink, pastels, or crayons, print something suitable to the occasion, or a quotation, proverb, or Bible verse. Decorate in colors as desired. On the reverse side write the name, date, and occasion.

A Thanksgiving Turkey

By Barbara Snow

Cut a 7-inch circle from light-weight cardboard. Make colored feathers from old magazine pages by tearing pieces about ½ inch wide and 2 inches long. Paste them by the end around the edge of the circle except where the body will be added. Continue adding overlapping rows till the circle is covered.

Cut the head and body from dark-brown construction paper. The beak, eye, and feet are cut from yellow paper, and the wattles from red paper. Paste them in the proper places. Then paste the body to the tail.

Perky Pilgrims

By Kathryn Heisenfelt

Select small, round whole walnuts for heads, larger half-shells for bodies. With red pencil draw a mouth on the dividing line, curving the corners for a smile. Remove stems and buds from whole cloves, and glue on the four-pointed remainders for eyes.

Man. Make legs of heavy white paper, 3½ by 2½ inches. Roll tightly widthwise, and glue. The pants are black paper, 6½ by 1¾ inches. Roll loosely widthwise, and glue over legs. Shoes are black paper, 6½ by 1 inch. Fold in half. Fold again, and again. Glue loose edges firmly. Run a pencil through to make circular opening. Place leg in shoe, and glue. Add yellow or gold paper buckles.

Mount the half-figure on a red paper circle, then glue to a slightly larger heavy cardboard circle.

Now glue a white paper collar to the top of the half-shell body. Glue the head to the collar. Make the hat of black paper with a white or gold paper buckle, and glue to the head. Glue white paper hands to the inside edge of the body.

Put glue on the inside of the body and place on top of the mounted half figure.

Lady. The skirt is gray paper, 6 by 2 inches. Gather the 6-inch side in folds. Glue to the inside of the half-shell body. Stuff skirt with a facial tissue. Glue it to a red paper circle, then to a larger cardboard circle. Glue a white paper kerchief to the top of the body. Then glue the head to the kerchief. Make a white paper cap and glue to the head. Glue white paper hands to the inside edge of the body.

Nut cups or place cards may be glued to the circle bases if desired.

Make a Mystic Boat

By Eulalia S. Hecox

Use a little wooden ice-cream spoon. With a sharp knife dig out enough of the wood underneath the spoon to hold a good-sized needle. Be sure not to cut through the spoon.

Stroke the needle on a magnet — always in the same direction and at the same end of the magnet. It may take fifty or more strokes. Test it now and then to be sure the needle is magnetized. Then paste it in the slot in the spoon with good glue.

Cut out a tiny paper sail. Bend the bottom of the sail ¼ inch down flat. Coat it with glue and stick it to the topside of the spoon.

Fill a large glass baking dish with water. When the glue is dry, set the boat in the water and use the magnet to pull the boat around without touching it.

Another kind of mystic boat may be made from good-sized corks, split lengthwise, or used upright. Stick the little sail on top and fill the bottom surface of the cork boat with thumbtacks. Use the magnet to make them do tricks.

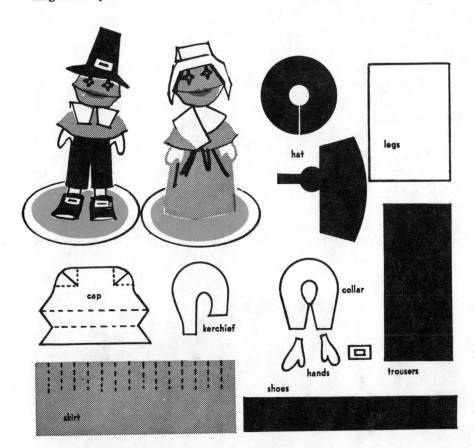

19

Creative Fun

Strip Pumpkin
By Lee Lindeman

This pumpkin is made from eight strips of orange construction paper 1 inch wide and 18 inches long. Place them on top of each other. Arrange as shown. Paste or staple together at the center.

Punch a hole at both ends of each strip. Bring ends together so strips form a pumpkin shape. Add an orange handle. Hold together with a two-prong paper fastener, running it through all holes. Add green paper leaves.

Indian Nut Cup
By Lee Lindeman

For this nut cup you will need a piece of cardboard tubing 3 inches high. Close one end of the tube by putting glue around the rim and placing it firmly on a piece of heavy paper. When the glue is dry, trim off the excess paper.

Use the top half of the cup for feathers and the bottom half for the face. Pencil in a double line for the headband, and sketch feathers from the top of the tube to the band. Cut between each feather down to the band. Carefully bend each feather out. Paint with tempera or poster paint.

Paint a face and hair on the lower half of the cup.

Dinosaur Skeleton
By Alice Gilbreath

A dinosaur skeleton is easy to make. You can have fun with it too because it glows in the dark!

You will need one disc from a turkey neck, several pipe cleaners, and some luminous paint. Clean the turkey neck disc by boiling it.

Join two pipe cleaners by twisting the ends together. Straighten them out to make the full-length "spine."

The rest of the parts are made by firmly twisting the center of the pieces twice around the spine.

Use one pipe cleaner for the arms and one for the legs. Add the ribs, tail, and toes. Cut them as shown in the drawing.

The turkey neck disc is the head. Push the pipe cleaner through the disc till the disc is about an inch from the front legs. Bend the pipe cleaner back under and twist it around the spine to form the neck. Cut off any pipe cleaner that is left over.

Paint the entire skeleton with luminous paint. When thoroughly dry, bend and curve the various parts as illustrated. With a little adjusting, the dinosaur skeleton will stand alone on its legs and tail. Take it in a dark closet, close the door, and LOOK!

Soap Sculpture

By Francine Litt Brown

The tools needed for soap sculpture are a medium-sized paring knife, and an orange stick.

Let white laundry soap stand for twenty-four hours to dry out. Then smooth the surface by gently removing the outer edges and lettering with the knife. Do the carving on a tray or large sheet of newspaper. Save the chips for household use.

Choose a simple design that does not need delicate carving or have too many parts extending out. These are easily broken off. The outline may be sketched right on the soap with the orange stick. Make a few cuts in the soap to block out the object, then cut away the soap that is not needed. Use the knife as if peeling a potato.

Always work on the whole form, turning it often. Don't try to finish any one part before working on another. Work slowly, and always do the big things first.

Be careful always to cut away in small slices. Soap tends to break if cut in large slices.

Outline all the important lines with the orange stick. Carve the lines nearest the surface first, then those farther in. Last of all, fill in the details with the orange stick.

Let the finished soap sculpture stand to dry for a day. Then polish it gently by rubbing it all over with a tissue and smoothing it gently with your fingertips and palms.

For a larger figure, join two cakes of soap together by scraping the sides to be joined until they are smooth and level. Put them in a shallow pan of water over a low heat for a few minutes. Then place a piece of sharp toothpick in the side that is to be joined, and press the two cakes together. Allow them to dry and harden for a few hours.

Be careful to place the toothpicks where they will not interfere with carving later. Broken pieces may be fixed in the same way.

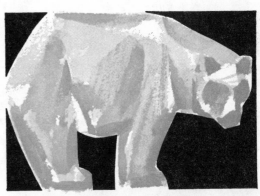

For Christmas Time

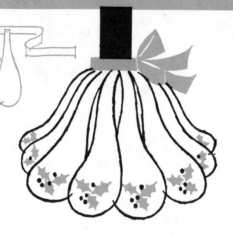

Tree Skirt
By Lee Lindeman

This skirt for your Christmas tree is fast and easy to make. You will need a strip of cloth or felt about 1½ yards long and 2 inches wide; also some strips of paper about 2 feet long and 6 inches wide.

From each strip of paper cut a large teardrop shape about 2 feet long. Staple the narrow end of a teardrop shape to the center of the strip of cloth. Repeat until there are about 9 inches left on each end of the strip.

Wrapping-ribbon Greeting Card
By Beatrice Bachrach

Draw and cut out a paper Christmas tree shape. Cover it with pieces of different colored gift wrapping ribbon, overlapping them as you paste. Trim off excess ribbon to the tree shape. The strips may be applied horizontally, vertically, or diagonally. Paste the tree to a folded piece of heavy construction paper. Add a glowing star of glitter at the top and a crayoned trunk at the bottom.

22

Decorate the end of each shape with holly, Christmas characters, or designs that you think are attractive.

Place the skirt around the bottom of the tree to cover the holder. Tie the cloth ends in a bow.

Christmas Tree
By June Rose Mobly

The trunk is a cardboard tube painted green with poster paint. Cut prongs on one end and stick them through holes cut in the center of a red inverted paper plate. Make branches by cutting a hole the size of the cylinder circumference in the center of five different-sized plates. Paint them green. Cut a jagged edge around the outside of these plates. Push them down on the trunk. Fasten the small one on top with pipe cleaner colored green.

Wreath
By Lee Lindeman

For a base, cut a large circle from a piece of heavy cardboard. Draw a smaller circle in the center and cut it out.

From bathroom tissue tubes, paper towel tubes, or waxed paper tubes, cut off 1-inch rings. You will need a great many of these rings. Cut a zigzag or scalloped edge on

one side of each ring. Glue the tube rings onto the cardboard base, zigzag edge up.

The whole wreath may be covered with these rings, or they can be grouped in threes and fours.

Paint the wreath with poster paint or spray with spray paint. A few pieces of holly cut from paper can be added. Red beads make the berries. Glue on a bright-colored paper bow.

Sponge Printing
By Barbara Deane

You can decorate your own gift wrapping paper and greeting cards with a printing stamp made from a discarded jar top and a flat kitchen sponge.

Draw a simple design, no larger than the jar top, on lightweight cardboard. Cut it out. Lay this pattern on top of the sponge and cut around it with a sharp knife or scissors. Glue the sponge design to the outside of the jar top, using strong glue.

Pour poster paint into a shallow dish. Cut a piece of white shelf paper large enough to cover the package you wish to wrap. Grasp the edge of the jar top and dip the sponge in the paint. Then press the sponge against the paper to print the design.

If you use different color combinations, print with one color all over the paper, and let it dry before printing with another color.

After the allover pattern is dry, additional details may be added. By dipping the eraser end of a pencil in the paint and pressing it on a Christmas tree shape, you can make colored lights or balls. You will think of many more such ideas as you work.

For greeting cards, cut construction paper in a rectangle. Fold it in half. Print the design on the outside and the greetings inside.

Pine Cone Candle Holder
By Lee Lindeman

Small pine cones help to make very attractive candle holders for the holidays.

From heavy corrugated cardboard cut two large circles about 4 inches in diameter. In the center of each, cut a hole about the size of a nickel. Test the size of the holes by fitting in them the candles you plan to use. Ten-inch candles will look well in these holders.

Glue the pine cones around the holes. When the glue is dry, remove the candles and spray the holders, including the cones, with gold or silver spray paint.

Tree Ornament
By Helen R. Sattler

Cut six drinking straws in half. Hold the twelve pieces together and wrap a piece of heavy thread, about 12 inches long, around the center of the bundle. Pull the thread as tightly as possible so the straws will stand out. Tie securely. Use the extra thread to hang the ornament by making a knot in the ends. Spread the straws apart. Spray with gold or silver paint.

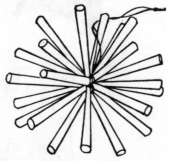

Jolly Santa Tissue Box
By Martha Utley Aitken

A Santa decoration on an unopened box of facial tissues will make a clever gift. Use red tissue paper folded double and long enough to cover the box and to extend beyond it for the hat as shown. Cover three sides and the fourth side only up to the slot through which the tissues will be removed. This side is now Santa's back. Gather the hat end, insert a cotton ball, and staple or tie firmly with thread.

For the face and beard, cut three pieces of white tissue wide enough to cover the front and overlap one inch on each side. Scallop the bottoms. Paste them separately so you

have three rows of scallops as shown. Make facial features with crayon.

The hat band is a white tissue strip, double thickness and about an inch wide, pasted around the box. The coat trim is another strip about a half inch wide pasted around the bottom and shaped in front as shown. The belt is black paper, with a buckle drawn with a gold-colored crayon.

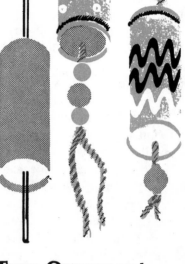

Christmas Angel Ornament

By Margaret Yates

Make a loop about the size of a dime in one end of a white pipe cleaner. Twist another pipe cleaner around the first one, just below the loop, and bend it to form shoulders and arms.

About 1½ inches from the middle of an 8-inch facial tissue cut a slit just large enough to let the loop through. Wrap the tissue around the pipe cleaners to form a gown. Tie it at the waist with thread or ribbon, leaving a long end at the back. Cut the tissue off at the bottom to make an even hemline.

Cut a pair of wings from aluminum foil or gold paper. Glue or tape to the back just above the waist.

Now pick the angel up by the string. If the head hangs down, attach one or more small buttons to the end of the pipe cleaner hidden by the gown. This will make the lower end heavier. The angel will hang horizontally or upright, depending on the size and number of buttons used.

For the book, crease the small rectangle of paper or foil in the middle and tape it between the hands. For the trumpet, roll a small piece of foil into a long cone.

Use the angel alone as a tree ornament, or make several and arrange them from thin wires or bamboo sticks to form a mobile.

Tree Ornaments

By Frances M. Callahan

Use miniature salt cartons for these ornaments.

Using an ice pick or awl, punch a hole in the center of the cardboard bottom. The top is plastic, and the point of the ice pick will have to be heated to make the hole in this end, so it should be done with the help of an older person.

Paint the outside of the carton with enamel. To hold the carton while painting, insert a swab stick in one of the holes. Two coats may be needed to cover the printing.

When the enamel is dry, decorate the sides and ends with odd bits of braid, glitter, and sequins, using white glue.

Make a pendant of glass Christmas beads, using a darning needle and a long piece of colored yarn or fancy string. Run the string through the holes in the carton, and make a 2-inch hanging loop as shown.

Santy Hanky for Dad

By Agnes Choate Wonson

Draw and paint a Santa face on a 6-by-8-inch white card. Cut along the bottom of the moustache. Glue on cotton moustache, eyebrows, and tuft on the cap.

Fold a man's handkerchief in half, pleat it along the fold, and insert in the slit under the moustache, as shown.

24

Cranberry Crunchies

By Jean LaWall

1 cup uncooked rolled oats
½ cup flour
1 cup brown sugar
½ cup butter or margarine
1-pound can cranberry sauce
(jellied or whole)

Mix oats, flour, and brown sugar in a bowl. Cut in the butter with a dull knife until the mixture is crumbly. Place half of this mixture in an 8-by-8-inch greased baking dish. Cover with all the cranberry sauce. Then spread the rest of the mixture over the top. Bake at 350 degrees for 45 minutes. Cut in squares and serve hot or cold, topped with a small scoop of vanilla ice cream.

Decorate a Flowerpot
By Evelyn Minshull

Paint a clean flowerpot with black enamel. Let it dry thoroughly.

Decorate with bits of bright-colored felt, strips of rickrack, yarn, or twine; beads, sequins, or small buttons. Use a heavy white glue. The size and type of design will depend on the size of the pot. Spray with lacquer or cover with clear plastic.

This makes a nice gift for anyone who likes house plants.

Snow Man Christmas Card
By Frances M. Callahan

The card is made from colored construction paper, 5½ by 8½ inches. Fold in each side 2 inches, then back one inch to the outside, so the card will stand.

Two balls of absorbent cotton (or flat cotton rolled) will make the snow man. Cut each ball in half. Use one half-section for the bottom of the snow man. From the other sections, peel off cotton for the smaller middle section, and even smaller head, and for snow across the bottom. Put glue on the card and paste the cotton in place.

Shape the hat from two pieces of black pipe cleaner. Cut tiny pieces of black pipe cleaner for buttons and facial features, and tiny pieces of white for snowflakes.

Use alphabet soup letters for the greeting. These and the other tiny pieces are more easily handled with tweezers. Dip them in glue and paste in place.

Angel Christmas Card By Barbara Baker

For these angel cards, gather together any fancy scraps you can find — pieces of net, plastic, felt, yarn, aluminum foil, sequins, ornaments, feathers, and the like.

Use a fold of heavy white paper for the card. On the front, paste the angel — triangle body, lace or net wings, round felt head, halo of foil, sequin decorations and feet. On the inside write your message.

Christmas Wreaths By Dorothe A. Palms

Cut the center out of two aluminum pie tins, leaving the rims plus two inches. Fringe 1½ inches of this two inches. The finer the fringe, the prettier it will be. This leaves ½ inch for a frame inside the rim.

Cut a circle from colored nylon net, the same size as the tin. Insert it tightly between the two tins. Staple the tins together. Push the fringe out and up, back over the rims on both sides.

Staple or tie a small cluster of Christmas balls or a corsage in the center of the net. Hang on the door or in a window.

Tiny wreaths may be made from individual frozen pie tins. Arrange several of them on the wall for room decorations.

Mr. and Mrs. Tree Ball By M. Mable Lunz

Use small pink or silver tree balls. Glue on a mouth and nose cut from black construction paper. Add tiny circles of blue pipe cleaner for eyes, and black pipe-cleaner eyebrows.

Mr. Tree Ball's top hat is made from a 1¼-inch length of cardboard tubing. Cut a circle of black construction paper a little larger than the open tube end. Clip around the circle, place it over the tube end, and glue it in place by the little tabs. Cover the rest of the crown with black paper.

Cut a 3-inch circle of black paper for the hat brim. Clip in from the center of the circle. Glue the tabs to the inside of the crown.

Attach a fine wire to the holder of the tree-ball head. Make a hole in the top of the hat at the front edge. Run the wire up through the hole. Loop the wire end for a hanger.

Glue the hat to the head at the desired angle. Tie a bow about 2½ inches wide, from narrow red ribbon. Glue it under the chin.

Mrs. Tree Ball is made the same except that the hat is made from a ¾-inch piece of tubing, covered with red or other bright-colored construction paper, with a band of ribbon and some artificial flowers added.

The chin bow matches the hatband. The ends of the ribbon extend up each side of the head and are glued under the hat. The wire hole in the hat is in the center, and the brim is turned down in front.

Leaf Designs

By Kathleen E. Little

Paste dried leaf branches to lightweight cardboard, using transparent gummed tape. At the bottom paste a bow or flowerpot cut from colored metallic paper. Decorate the "tree" with gummed stars or other cutouts.

Flickering Holiday Candle By Barbara Snow

Cover a toilet tissue tube with paper. Tape or glue it securely. Use gift wrapping paper or decorate plain or colored paper with your own designs.

Cut two identical flames from red construction paper. Insert a 6-inch piece of thread between them, lengthwise, and paste them together.

Cut two 3½-inch halos from yellow construction paper. Cut out the centers as illustrated. Cover one with glue. Center the flame in the hole. Lay the thread ends across the glue, and add the other halo. Trim off the leftover thread ends.

Cut two slits in the candle. Slide the halo into the slits, with the flame straight up in the center. A breath of air on the flame will make it seem to flicker.

Egg Cup Santa By Florence Hodges

Here is a fat, jolly Santa made from egg cartons, cotton, and paint.

Cut an egg carton open and remove four of the egg cup sections. Be sure to cut them apart below the portion of carton which joins one cup to another so that you have only the round bottom half.

Color three of these cups red on the outside with poster paint or crayon. Leave one white.

Glue two of the red sections together where they have been cut. Glue the third section on top of the white one, again joining at the cut part.

Twist some cotton into a thick cord and glue this around the seams you have made on the cups. The cotton on the top half makes Santa's fur-trimmed hat. On the bottom half, it is his jacket trim. With cotton make a tassel for his hat, buttons for his coat, hair, and whiskers.

With paint or crayon, color his eyes, nose, and mouth.

Glue the two halves together.

The Good Shepherd By Betty Merritt

For the body, cut a 12-inch circle from three thicknesses of newspaper. Fold them in half. Form into a cone not more than 2½ inches across the bottom. Cover the outside with white crepe paper, and the inside with a folded circle of white.

For the head, use a ball of cotton, covered with flesh-colored crepe paper. Fasten to the tip of the cone.

The arms are a 5-inch roll of newspaper, pencil thick. Each hand is a square of flesh-colored paper, folded down from the top, and from the sides to the center. Twist them at the wrist and fasten to the arm ends. Cover arms with white paper.

Make the mantle or cloak from bright-red paper about 5 inches wide and twice the length of the body. Slit it about halfway up the center front and fold over the arms as shown, leaving the robe full length and width in back.

Paste on beard and long hair made from fringed brown paper. Add features in ink, with eyes far apart.

The staff is a 12-inch colored pipe cleaner, bent to shape shown, and fastened to the hand and the bottom of the white robe.

Stained-glass Windows

By Dorothy Scott Milke

Materials required are a roll of white shelf paper, all the broken crayons you can find, and a bottle of baby oil or liquid shortening.

The examples shown use the three wise men as the theme, but angels, shepherds, or the nativity scene are all adaptable.

Cut the shelf paper in lengths suitable for your window. Arch each panel at the top. Make a small drawing of the scene you wish to use. Enlarge it, and transfer it with pencil to the white paper. Draw over the pencil lines heavily, about a quarter of an inch in width, with black crayon.

After this "leading" is drawn in, decide on the color to be used in each marked-off area. Then color each section completely, bearing down hard on the crayon to get as deep a color and as opaque a covering as possible.

When all the panels are completed, turn them face down on a newspaper-covered table, one at a time, and give them a coating of oil, applying it with small wads of cotton. The oil gives the translucent effect of stained glass when the panels are hung in a window. Fasten them to the glass with half-inch masking tape all around the edges to keep them from curling.

28

Christmas Tree

By Lee Lindeman

Make a half circle from an 18-by-24-inch piece of heavy paper. Shape the half circle into a cone. Staple or tape together. Be sure that the cone will stand straight.

Fold in half the long way a 6-by-24-inch strip of green tissue paper or colored cellophane. On the fold cut a series of slits 1 inch deep and about ½ inch apart. Unfold, and then fold the opposite way, but do not crease. Make a number of these strips.

Attach one end of a strip to the top of the cone. Carefully wind it around the cone, taping the end. Start the next strip so there will be no gap. Continue winding these strips around the cone until it is completely covered. Carefully fluff out the loops. Add an ornament at the top.

A Hanging Garden

By Jean LaWall

Tie a bright ribbon securely to a large, firm apple so that it can be hung up. Collect several different kinds of evergreens, except holly which will not live in the apple juice. Push the greens firmly into the apple, all around. Hang it in a window or doorway. The apple will keep the greens fresh and pretty.

A Candle Snuffer

By Ruth Everding Libbey

Wrap a piece of stiff wire around the metal top from a small-mouthed bottle such as a ketchup bottle. Twist the wire firmly around the top, then twist the two ends together to make a handle 6 or 7 inches long. Wrap a piece of tape or glue a narrow piece of cloth around the handle end so the wire will not scratch.

Christmas Cornucopias

By Deirdre B. Watkins

Use a piece of fairly stiff paper (construction paper, gift wrapping foil, or a colorful Christmas card). Cut to 5 or 6 inches square. When using Christmas cards, cut your square with the corners at the center top, bottom, and sides of the picture.

Roll into a cone. Paste down the long edge, using a paper clip until the paste dries. When pasting the pointed end, insert your scissors points and press against them.

Make a small hole at the back and insert a narrow ribbon or colored string to form a hanging loop.

A strip of tissue paper about 2 inches wide can be pasted around the inside at the top and tucked into the center, or the part of the inside which shows can be lined with contrasting paper. A plain cornucopia can be decorated with metallic rickrack, Christmas seals, or medallions cut from Christmas cards.

These "horns of plenty" can be hung on the tree, or filled with candy or small gifts such as hankies.

Santa Mailbag

By Dorothy Anderson Burge

Put your Christmas cards in a special Santa bag this Christmas. Hung on a doorknob or the wall of your room, it makes a gay decoration.

Use a brown grocery bag about 6 by 11 inches in size. Cut and paste red construction paper to cover the lower three-fourths of the bag front.

The face is a 4-inch pink circle cut from construction paper. The cap is a red triangle with one side as wide as the bag front. Paste this side along the top edge with the rest of the cap extending beyond the bag. Paste a 1-inch white circle on the peak of the cap, and a ¾-inch white strip on the bottom for fur.

Add blue paper ovals for eyes, a black nose, and a red mouth. The beard, mustache, and eyebrows are white cotton. Paste on white paper mittens, cuffs, and buttons.

On the back of the bag near the top stick two gummed reinforcements about 2 inches apart. Make a hole through the centers and string ribbon through for hanging.

Embossed Ornaments and Wall Plaques

By Dorothy Anderson Burge

Ornaments. Cut off the rim from a thin aluminum pan used for baked goods. Place this trimmed circle, wrong side up, on several thicknesses of newspaper. With a ball-point pen that no longer contains ink, draw or trace a design on the aluminum. With a wooden stick, smooth out the portions of the design inside the lines. Press very firmly, going over and over the inside of the design to stretch the aluminum until it is raised or "embossed" on the other side.

Turn the circle over and place it on a table or other hard surface. With the pen or stick, retrace the outside lines and any lines inside the design. Smooth out the area outside the design with a wide stick. When finished, shine by rubbing gently with a wet, soap-filled steel-wool pad.

To make a fancy edge, cut slashes an equal distance apart all around the edge of the circle. Curl every other section forward over a pencil. Curl the rest toward the back. Punch a hole in the edge and insert a piece of colored wool or ribbon for a hanger.

The triangular sections in TV dinner plates may also be used in this way for small ornaments.

Plaques. Draw a picture that will fill the circle within ¼-inch of the edge. Emboss as described above. Bend the edge forward all around to form the frame.

Gifts for Mother

By Lee Lindeman

Beads From Tissue

Bits of toilet tissue or paper napkins can be made into a very attractive and lightweight bead necklace.

In a cup mix about ¼ cup water and about 2 teaspoons of some creamy white glue. Dip two squares of toilet tissue into the glue mixture. Then wrap them around a round toothpick (or a needle or pin), squeezing out the excess moisture as you shape the bead. Squeeze tightly and carefully. When the bead is shaped, carefully pull out the needle, pin, or toothpick. Repeat this until you have enough beads for a necklace. Let the beads dry for a day or two until they are hard.

Paint with tempera paint, plain or multicolored. When dry, coat with clear lacquer or nail polish. String them on dental floss or on strong gold or silver thread.

If the necklace is long enough to slip over the head, tie the ends together. If it is short, attach a catch from an old necklace to the ends.

Place Mats

Paint or color a picture on a piece of heavy paper, 12 by 18 inches. Use bright colors.

Cut two pieces of clear plastic large enough so that there will be a ½-inch border of plastic all around the picture.

Use a needle with button thread to sew around the edge of the place mat, making even, straight stitches. The stitches should hold the two pieces of plastic together with the picture on the inside. Be sure that you keep the two pieces of plastic and the picture smooth and straight as you sew.

You can make place mats for everyone in your family.

Felt-flower Earrings

Cut small petals from colored felt. Glue them to a dime-sized piece of stiff paper. Use a piece of felt of contrasting color for the center of the flower. When dry, carefully glue them to earring backs that you have obtained from a variety store.

String and Tissue Fun

By Lee Lindeman

You will need plain or colored tissue paper, white creamy glue, heavy white string or cord, or thin yarn.

Put some of the glue in a cup and add a tiny bit of water. Mix thoroughly.

Cut the string into 1- or 2-foot lengths. Soak the pieces in the glue. Squeeze out the excess by pulling the string between your fingers.

On a piece of tissue paper, place the glue-soaked string in an interesting shape. Use the shapes shown, or make some of your own. Carefully place another piece of tissue paper on top of the design. Press down gently along the string. When the string dries, it will be very stiff.

Trim the tissue paper close to the dried string. Decorate with paint and glitter.

These tissue designs can be used in a mobile, as an ornament for the Christmas tree, or to hang in the window.

Christmas Crib

By Sister Mary Norma

On gray or brown construction paper, measure and draw the lines shown in the diagram. Cut on the heavy lines, fold on the dotted lines, and paste as pictured. Fold green paper and cut two smaller trees and two larger ones, on the fold. Staple the two small trees together at the fold, then the two large ones. Paste one on each side of the stable.

Draw and color a nativity scene. Cut it out, including the bottom strip shown. Paste the ends of the strip together, then to the inside back of the shed. Paste a gold star at the top of the stable.

Fig.B

Fig.C

Fig.A

Fig.D

Fig.E

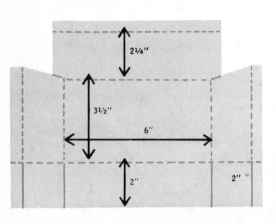

Stained Glass Windows

By Marsha West

You will need sheets of black construction paper, 12 by 18 inches; red, blue, green, and yellow cellophane, transparent cellophane tape, and newspaper or wrapping paper for making patterns.

First cut out a pattern for the window itself. Fold lengthwise a piece of paper the same size as the construction paper. Cut to a tapered point as shown in Figure A. Trace around the pattern on black construction paper and cut out neatly.

Next, plan the design. Use one large shape for the center and arrange smaller shapes such as Christmas trees, bells, and stars around it.

A fancy star may be made by folding a square of paper in half twice, then once more to make a triangle. Cut on the solid lines only, as shown in Figure B. When it is unfolded, it will look like Figure C.

For bells and trees, fold the paper once, lengthwise, and cut as shown in Figures D and E.

Arrange the patterns on the black window shape so they are centered and balanced. Then trace around them and cut out carefully. Tape the pieces of colored cellophane in place to fill the cut-out shapes. Cut the edges of the cellophane straight and tape them neatly so that the back of the window will be attractive, too.

Hang or tape the window to the glass pane. Sunlight from outside or artificial light from indoors at night will make the windows glow with jewel-like colors.

Spatter Cards and Cutout Cards

By Tena M. Nelson

Materials

Use poster paint or finger paint in light colors for dark paper, and dark colors for light paper. The paint should be "soupy."

All-purpose glue that comes in a bottle with a spout can be used to paste glitter as well as paper. Flour paste doesn't stick well and tends to warp the paper.

Other materials needed are a small piece of screen, an old toothbrush, gummed stars, glitter, and construction paper in all colors.

Card Folders

Fold 9-by-12-inch construction paper, top to bottom, then side to side, to make the card folder. For long cards, fold the paper in thirds to 9-by-4 inches, then cut off the third section.

Patterns

Design your own shapes, or cut them from magazines or old Christmas cards. Turn them over. If you can tell what the shapes are, they will make good patterns. Use them for both spatter and cutout cards.

Spatter Cards

The paint really does spatter, so choose a place where you can make plenty of mess. Cover the working space with newspaper. Place a large piece of cardboard on it.

Lay the folder on the cardboard, arrange the pattern on it, and fasten it through to the cardboard with straight pins. Moisten the toothbrush and scoop up a little paint—not too much or it will drop off in big drops. Grasp the screen in the left hand between thumb and first finger. Hold it about six inches from the card, and at a slight angle. Run the toothbrush back and forth over the screen. Keep it moving rapidly. Clean the underside of the screen when paint accumulates. Spatter a thick layer of paint on the card. Let it dry before removing the pins.

Cutout Cards

Select the pattern or patterns for each card. Trace around them on different colors of construction paper, cut out, and glue to the folder. For some figures like the Madonna, use different colors for different parts.

Variations and Decorations

Combine designs such as candy cane and wreath, or sled and bells.

Decorate cutout cards and unpainted parts of spatter cards with glitter, bits of metallic paper, cotton, or gummed stars.

Use the inside for the message.

Candy and Nut Cups
By Ella L. Langenberg

Make a heart pattern (Figure 1) by folding a 2¼-inch square diagonally as shown. Cut off the shaded area. .

Fold a 4½-inch square of heavy white paper in half twice as shown in Figure 2. Trace around the pattern on the four sections of the white paper. Cut off the shaded area. Then cut to the center on one fold as shown by the heavy line (Figure 2).

Cut three smaller red hearts and paste them on three of the white ones. Paste the fourth white heart over the first one, on the inside, to form a three-sided cup. See Figure 3.

Tie the sides together with narrow ribbon or thread. Push up the point at the bottom so the cup will stand.

Valentine Man
By Joyce T. Buckner

Draw a large heart on folded white construction paper, with the top of the heart at the dotted lines, as shown. Cut out on the solid lines only. Write a message on the inside heart. Paint the outside heart red. For each eye, use a lining from a pop bottle cap. Place a small wad of paper on it, then wrap with white tissue paper. Add white paper nose and mouth. Draw on the rest of the eye and the eyebrow with paint or crayon.

Valentine Basket
By Mavis Grant

Select two white lace paper doilies. The size depends on the size of basket desired. Cut two red construction paper circles, a half inch or so smaller than the doilies. Paste the doilies to the circles, right side down. Then overlap them about halfway, and paste. Fold as shown.

Decorate the red paper handle with cutouts from a third doily. Paste the ends to the inside of the basket.

34

Apple Valentine

By Katherine Corliss Bartow

Cut an apple shape from a fold of red construction paper, leaving the left side on the fold uncut so it will open like a book.

Cut two leaves from green paper. Draw black veins. Glue the leaves to the apple.

Cut a ¾-inch piece of brown pipe cleaner for the stem. Glue one end to the inside front.

With white ink, make a heart on the front, with initials inside, and an arrow.

Inside, make freehand white ink drawings. Print your message: "An Apple for My Valentine," "You Are the Apple of My Eye," or "An Apple for My Teacher."

Add touches, and outline the heart with glitter.

Pin Valentines

By Ellen E. Morrison

Cut a valentine heart about 4 inches wide from construction paper — any color but red. Cut a smaller heart from red paper, about 1 inch wide. Fasten the smaller heart onto the large heart with a shiny straight pin. Then letter on the large valentine heart one of these messages:

> I'll gladly pin my hopes on you
> To be my Valentine so true.
>
> My happiness de-pins on you
> So won't you be my Valentine true?

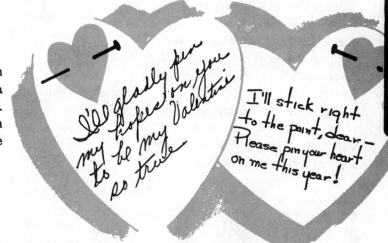

Valentines

By Dorothe A. Palms

Cut a large heart shape from cardboard. Cut two white or colored construction paper hearts, the same size. Glue a small amount of cotton in the center of the cardboard heart. Paste on the paper hearts, front and back. Decorate as desired. Finish with a bow at the top or in the middle of the valentine. Glue a small paper heart at the end of each streamer.

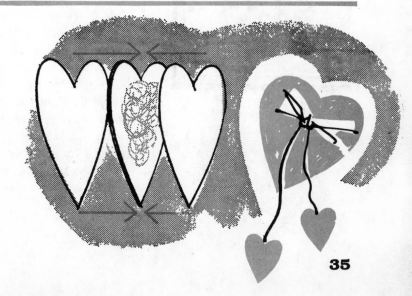

35

Things To Make

A Pin-pricked Valentine

By Agnes Choate Wonson

Cut a heart shape from a folded piece of red construction paper so that the top of the heart is on the fold.

Lay tracing paper over the folded heart and print a message to fit the card. Turn the tracing paper over so the message reads backwards.

Place the double heart and tracing paper on a piece of heavy corrugated cardboard. With a heavy darning needle or large pin, prick holes along the pencil lines through tracing paper and both hearts. This will give an interesting embossed effect on the front of the card. A paper lace edge may be added to the red heart if desired.

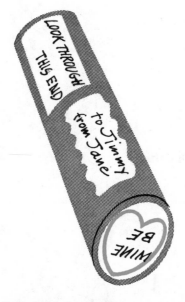

Spyglass Valentine

By Martha Carpenter

This valentine is made from a cardboard tube such as is found in rolls of paper towels or waxed paper. Color the tube with paint or crayon.

Make two labels, one to read "Look Through This End" and the other to read "To ____ From ____." Glue on the labels.

Place one end of the tube on a piece of tracing paper or tissue paper, and trace a circle. Inside this circle draw a heart and print "Be Mine." Cut out the circle and fasten it to one end of the tube with common pins stuck into the cardboard. The message should be placed so that it can be read by looking into the spyglass when the spyglass is being held up to the light.

Gumdrop Flowers for Cookies

By Ursula Kannry

To make pretty decorations for cookies, you will need soft gumdrops of different colors, granulated sugar, and a rolling pin and breadboard. Sprinkle sugar onto the board. Cut a gumdrop in half and place half on the board. Roll this into a 2½-inch-long strip, turning the gumdrop after each stroke so that it will not stick.

Roll the strip with your fingers, pinching one side of it to form a stem. This will cause the other side to spread out like the petals of a blossom. Try two half-strips of different colors for a two-toned flower. Press onto a flat cooky.

Green gumdrops can be cut and pressed onto the cooky for leaves.

Window Shade Pulls
By Texie Hering

From green felt cut four leaves and one stem. From contrasting colored felt cut two flower shapes like the pattern, with a hole in the center as shown. Cut a circle of corrugated paper with a hole in the center to go between these flower shapes.

Push a colored glass marble into the hole of the paper circle. Loop a 16-inch length of colored string and knot the ends together. Paste the knotted end of the loop around the marble. Add the tips of the leaves and stem to the circle as shown. Then paste on the flower shapes, one on each side of the circle. Outline the petal shapes of the flowers with white ink or paint.

Attach to the window shade in place of your present pull, and see how prettily the light shines through the marble.

Calendar Race
By Irene D. Messman

Save the sheets that are torn off the calendar each month. Paste them on cardboard. Leave some sheets whole. Cut the numbers apart on the others. Put the loose numbers from each sheet in an envelope.

Have a race to see who can first put the correct numbers in the right place on the uncut calendar sheet. Then have a race to see who can first put the cut numbers in proper calendar order without a calendar sheet to go by.

Texture Pictures
By Marilyn Burch

Gather objects which possess different textures, such as small stones, a piece of sponge, burlap, paper grass, sand, bark, or colored paper. Choose a lid from a cardboard box. The picture will be made inside this lid.

Design a picture which contains textures of things you have collected. With the above material you might make a seashore scene. The water and sky might be blue tissue paper; the beach, sand and pebbles pasted in place; the treetop, a sponge; and a cabin, a piece of bark. When the picture is completed, stretch clear cellophane over the top of the lid. Use your imagination and make your own collection of texture pictures.

Valentines With Plastic Strips
By Lee Lindeman

Cut a valentine from very stiff colored paper or thin stiff cardboard. Plan a design with a pencil, making pencil dots in the places you are going to punch holes. With a paper punch, make holes through which to weave thin plastic strips.

Thin strips can be cut from plastic bleach or liquid soap bottles. Weave strips through the holes, starting and ending at the back of the card.

String a Heart
By Lee Lindeman

Cut a heart shape from construction paper or thin colored cardboard.

Cut some heavy string into 1- or 2-foot lengths. In a cup mix one tablespoon of white creamy glue with ½ tablespoon of water. Soak the string in the glue mixture for ten minutes. Pull a piece of string through your fingers to squeeze out the excess moisture. Quickly but carefully place the gluey string in an interesting arrangement on your valentine. Carefully press the string with your fingers, and let dry. Your string design could be a border along the edge of a valentine or it could be a design in the center.

Make-It Fun

Make Your Own Valentine

By Ella L. Langenberg

Select a lace paper doily, oblong or square. Make a folder from red construction paper, a little larger than the doily.

Cut a paper heart pattern smaller than the plain center of the doily. Trace around it on a piece of thin cardboard. Carefully cut out the heart shape and discard it. The rest of the cardboard is the stencil.

Mark a thick layer of red crayon around the edge of the heart. Place the stencil over the center of the doily. Holding it firmly in place, stroke the eraser end of a pencil from the edge of the heart to the center. The red crayon will rub off, making an interesting design as shown. Write a message or name on the heart.

Paste white paper inside the red folder, using just a little paste across the top. Write your own valentine verse on the white paper.

Little Nut Animals

By Texie Hering

These little animals may be made into lapel pins by sewing a small safety pin to a piece of felt. Then glue the felt to the back of the nut. Or they may be made into toys by using pipe cleaner legs.

Use pecan nuts of the right size for the head and body. Paint the facial features. Head and body may be left the natural nut color, or painted as desired. Glue on felt ears, feet, and tail.

If pipe cleaners are used for legs or other parts, make a hole in the shell for each part and insert the pipe cleaner with a little glue on it. Bend into shape after the glue has dried.

Puzzle Fun

By Alice Phelan

Would you like to make your little brother or sister a present that will amuse him and teach him to spell at the same time?

You need some old magazines and a piece of white cardboard. Cut out a large picture of a dog and paste it to the cardboard, leaving about two inches at the left side for lettering. Next, cut out three large letters D, O, and G. Paste them to the left of the cardboard, next to the picture, with the D at the top, the O in the middle, and the G at the bottom. Trim the cardboard, then cut across it so that one letter is on each of three

equal pieces. Now you have a simple puzzle that your small brother or sister can take apart and put together, at the same time learning how to spell DOG. If the name of the animal is put together wrong, the picture will be wrong, so even a quite young child will learn quickly to put it together properly.

When he tires of this puzzle, have one ready with CAT on it. Pretty soon he will be ready for four-letter puzzles such as LION and BEAR and DOLL or even five-letter puzzles such as TIGER and ZEBRA and HOUSE.

38

Valentine Nut Cups and Place Cards

By Dorothy Anderson Burge

For a party or for the family on Valentine Day, make nut cups and place cards, using cardboard tubes from bathroom tissue or paper towels.

Nut Cups

Cut the bathroom-tissue tube in half, or the paper-towel tube in fourths. Trace around the bottom of one tube on black construction paper. Cut out the circle and tape it to the tube to form the bottom of the cup. Cover the rest of the tube with black construction paper.

Cut a 3-by-3-inch heart from red construction paper. On the heart, paste eyes, ears, mouth, and nose made from gummed reinforcement rings. Cut the rings, as shown, to form these features. Half rings, stuck on the back of the heart, make a scalloped edge for hair. Sequins or beads may be tied or sewed through the ears for earrings. Paste this heart face to the black cup. Fill the cup with nuts or valentine candy.

Place Card Napkin Rings

Slit a paper tube down the middle. Cut it into 1-inch strips. Cover each strip with black paper. Cut a 2-by-2-inch heart from red paper. Make two horizontal slits, each about 1¼-inch wide, one above the other, in the heart. Print a name on the heart with crayon. Slide the black strip through the slits so that the heart stands up. Decorate with gummed reinforcement rings. A paper napkin, pinched in the center to form a bow, will fit in this napkin ring and help to decorate the table too.

Button Valentines

By Katherine Corliss Bartow

On folded red construction paper draw around a heart pattern, the pattern top being on the fold.

Choose two smooth, large, white, two-holed buttons. Paint eyes, mouth, and cheeks with ink, nail polish, or a felt marker.

For the nose, run pink yarn through the holes and knot in back.

Glue the buttons onto the valentine. For hair, glue on yellow yarn snips.

On the front of the card print "You're Cute as a Button." Inside print "Sew Let's Be Valentines."

Valentine Jack-in-the-box

By Florence Hodges

This matchbook valentine will pop up when opened. The jumping jack can be a heart cut from paper, or a heart with a verse on it cut from an old valentine, or your picture. Cut a strip of heavy construction paper 8 inches long and ⅝ inch wide. Fold it back and forth into ½-inch sections to form a spring. Glue the heart or face to the top section. Glue the bottom section to the inside back of an empty matchbook.

If the matchbook is not plain inside, paste construction paper over it. Cover the outside too, or just paste a valentine design over the printing.

Decorate the design with glued-on glitter or with paints or crayons. On the inside of the cover write a verse or greeting.

Valentine Bird

By Mavis Grant

Using red construction paper, cut one large heart for the bird body, one small heart for the tail, one medium-sized heart cut in half for wings, and a head shape as pictured. Paste as shown. Slash the beak and insert a red or white ribbon. On it string decorated valentines of different sizes.

Valentines With Tissue Paper

This valentine has fluffy three-dimensional flowers made from tissue paper.

Cut a large heart from heavy paper. Poke holes around the edge of the heart. Into these holes push the paper flowers.

The flowers are made by cutting colored tissue paper into 3-inch circles. Pinch the center of the circle and push the pinched end through one of the holes in the heart—just enough to tape the end to the back of the heart.

Use circles of different colors for a two-toned flower. Add green tissue paper leaves.

Valentines

By Lee Lindeman

In the Bag

Brown paper bags make wonderful valentine mail sacks. Roll the edge of the bag to make a kind of collar. This makes the bag a little stronger so it won't rip when the postman delivers your valentines.

Decorate the sack with your own designs. These can be cut out of colored construction paper and pasted on the bag. Perhaps you would rather use paint or crayon.

Use gummed tape or masking tape to fasten the valentine bag to your chair at school.

String a Valentine

Put some white glue in a cup. Add a tiny bit of water and mix. Soak pieces of string, 12 inches long, in the glue for about ten minutes. Squeeze out the excess glue by pulling the string between two fingers. Arrange a piece of glue-soaked string in the shape of a heart on a piece of colored tissue paper. Put another piece of tissue paper on top. Press down carefully. When the string dries between the tissue, it becomes stiff and hard.

Trim the tissue valentine. This can be used just as it is or as part of a mobile. Try other shapes also.

To make something really different, cut out a large valentine from cardboard. Save the outside rim. Suspend your tissue and string creation inside this rim. Thread is looped through the top and bottom of the tissue heart, and secured to the back of the cardboard rim with gummed tape. The tissue heart will twist and turn.

40

A Valentine With a Gift Pocket

Using heavy construction paper, cut a heart shape about the size of your hand. Cut another piece in the shape of the bottom of the heart. Put paste on the two side edges of this piece and paste it to the bottom of the large heart to form a pocket.

Decorate the heart as you wish. Put a handkerchief or other gift in the pocket of this unusual valentine.

Tasty Valentines

Make some plain heart-shaped cookies, or buy some at a bakery. To decorate them, you will need three or four empty cups; powdered sugar, a little water, and food coloring; and a small, clean paintbrush.

In each cup put 2 teaspoonfuls of powdered sugar, 1 drop of food coloring, and ½ teaspoon of water. Mix. The mixture should be as thick and runny as melted ice cream.

Now paint your designs on the cookies with the sugar mixture. Be sure that your brush is very clean. When the mixture dries, it will be a delicious icing on your tasty valentines.

A Valentine Mobile

From heavy construction paper, cut a circle about the size of a dinner plate. Then cut around and around the circle, spiraling into the center, as shown.

Tie one end of the spiral with a piece of thread or string, and suspend the mobile.

Small hearts or other shapes are cut from paper and hung on the mobile with thread. Watch them dance in the breeze.

A Mosaic Valentine

Cut a heart shape from heavy construction paper or cardboard. Plan and draw a simple design on the heart.

Cut or tear a variety of colored papers into very small pieces. With paste or glue, fasten these small pieces to the heart, filling in the design.

Eggshell Valentines

Save and clean a few empty eggshells. Pull off and discard any of the white membrane that may be on the inside of the shell.

Place the clean shells between two sheets of paper and roll over them with a rolling pin until they are crushed to the size of coarse sand.

Cut a heart from heavy construction paper or cardboard. Plan and draw a design on the paper heart. Put a thin, even layer of glue in the areas where you would like to have the eggshell texture. Sprinkle the crushed eggshells onto the moist glue. Pat the eggshells down carefully. Gently tip the paper and shake off the excess.

The white eggshell texture against red or pink paper makes an attractive valentine.

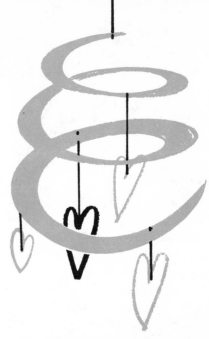

Heart Take
By Ida M. Pardue

For this Valentine Day game, cut six paper hearts for each player, and one extra. The extra heart should be black. The other hearts may be any color.

Put all the hearts in a paper sack. Players take turns reaching into the sack without peeking, and taking out one heart.

Whoever gets the black heart puts it back in the bag, and drops out of the game. The player staying in the game the longest wins.

Creatures of Fantasy
By Luella Pierce

Place the hand on a piece of 9-by-12 inch construction paper and trace around it, with colored crayon. Draw a head and add any other features desired, using different colors.

By placing the hand in different positions on the paper, many variations can be made. It is interesting to see how many different creatures the shape of a hand will suggest.

Folded Valentine
By Betsy Ann Page

Use a strip of construction paper 4 by 12 inches. Mark the corners A, B, C, and D, as in Figure 1.

Bring corners A and B together, and crease. Mark the crease line E-F as shown.

Open the strip, and fold on line A-E, then on line B-F, Figure 2. Refold on line E-F.

Cut heart shape as indicated by heavy lines in Figure 3.

Decorate as desired. Print **Be My Valentine** or other appropriate wording on the front, and a verse, such as the following, on the inside:

> If you were only here
> I'd whisper in your ear,
> "You are my Valentine!"

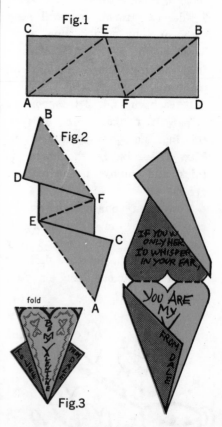

Cereal Box Village   By Gail Cottingham Koch

All the buildings are individual-sized cereal boxes, painted with different colors of enamel, and decorated by hand or with cutouts. The tall, narrow building is one box pasted on top of another, with the narrow side facing forward. The lowest building is a box resting on its side. The peaked roofs are made by cutting a box in half, diagonally. Paint them separately in black. Each chimney is made of a 2-by-4-inch strip of red construction paper rolled into a tube and inserted into a round hole cut in the roof, after the roof paint is dry.

Paste the buildings, in the order desired, to a narrow board painted black.

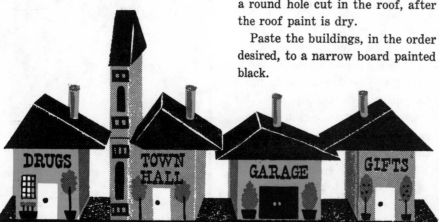

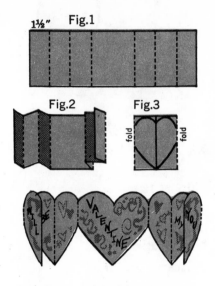

Another Folded Valentine
By Betsy Ann Page

Use a strip of construction paper 3½ by 12 inches. Measure fold lines 1½ inches apart as shown in Figure 1.

Fold each side toward the center, Figure 2.

Keeping the paper folded, cut a heart shape as shown by the heavy lines in Figure 3. Be sure NOT to cut the sections marked "fold."

On the front halves of the heart, print **Will** on one side and **You** on the other. Open the halves, and print **Be** and **My** on the second heart. On the inside heart, print **Valentine?**

Decorate as desired.

Crepe Paper Valentine
By Florence Hodges

This idea can be used for a Valentine Day decoration, or it can be made into a large valentine for a very important person.

Bend a wire coat hanger into a heart shape. Straighten out the hook and use that part of the hanger on one of the sides of the heart as support for the arrow end.

Cut a package of red crepe paper into 1¾-inch strips along the folds. Twist these papers around the hanger, pushing each piece up tight against the next until the entire hanger is covered.

Cut an arrow from heavy white paper. Glue it to the heart, with the shaft covering the straightened hook.

Valentine Mobiles
By Evelyn Green

Fold red, pink, or white construction paper in half, and cut out a large heart. With the heart still folded, cut out narrower heart shapes as shown. Open the hearts and arrange them as illustrated. Using every other heart makes the mobile more interesting. Lay a colored string or thread along the creases, being sure to leave an end long enough for hanging. Using transparent glue, paste each heart to the string. Let it dry thoroughly before hanging.

Try cutting several solid hearts of different sizes, pasting them on a string as shown.

Mr. and Mrs. Valentine
By Hazel H. Torbert

From red and white construction paper cut different sizes of heart shapes.

Look at the illustrations. Notice that some of the heart shapes have been cut in half. Now arrange the hearts to make Mr. and Mrs. Valentine.

When the arrangement is satisfactory, paste the hearts on sheets of colored paper.

Balancing Bird

By Jenny Pringle

This balancing bird will cling to your finger or to the edge of a cup. Make it from lightweight cardboard. Tape two pennies to each wing tip as shown.

Easter Egg Basket

By Judith LaDez

On a 9-by-12-inch sheet of heavy white paper, sketch lightly the lines shown in the diagram. Cut along these lines.

From colored construction paper cut seven 4½-by-⅝-inch strips. Weave these strips through the long slits in the white paper to form a basket as shown. Paste the top and bottom ends of the strips to the white paper.

An 11-inch paper strip of a darker color is needed for the handle. Gently bend it in half. Paste one half against the white paper, and the tip of the free half under the center weaving strip as shown.

Using the egg pattern, cut several eggs from construction paper of pastel colors. Decorate the eggs

with crayon, leaving the tab plain. Insert the egg tabs in the slits above the basket, and paste the tabs on the backside of the white paper.

Bend the handle and eggs forward so they stand away from the background.

Decorated Notepaper

By Jeanne Rueter

Wet a piece of typing paper by dipping it in and out of water. Lay the wet paper on a work surface. While it is still wet, use colored chalk to make various designs and marks on the paper for an allover mottled effect.

While this is drying, make notepaper folders from construction paper to fit your envelopes.

Cut the dry chalked paper into pieces smaller than the folder. Use your ruler to guide you. Glue one of the pieces of the chalk paper on each folder. Outline the chalk work with a felt marking pen or leave it plain.

Put a folder with each envelope. A set of eight or twelve makes a nice gift.

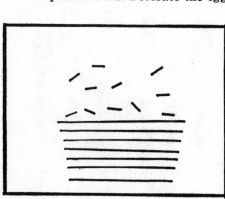

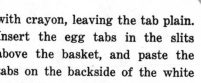

Lollipop Daisies

By Texie Hering

Use medium-sized lollipops wrapped in cellophane. For each lollipop you will need a strip of green crepe paper ½ inch wide and 5 inches long, cut lengthwise of the paper. Glue one end of the strip at the top of the stick near the candy. Wind around the stick, inserting green crepe paper leaves as shown, and secure the end with glue.

Cut two colored construction paper flower shapes like the pattern shown. Cut out the centers. Outline these centers and the petals with harmonizing colored crayon. Glue one on each side of the wrapped candy. Put bobby pins on the petal tips till dry.

Make the holder from corrugated cardboard and glue it to a place card. Slip the stem in the center hole of the corrugated holder.

Yarn and Cardboard Design

By Donald H. Hoffman

Use three pieces of colored yarn or string 4 to 8 feet long, a piece of shirt cardboard, and crayons to produce an interesting design.

Cut three or four slits ¼ to ½ inch deep into the edge on each side of the cardboard. Take the first piece of yarn and begin placing through the slits and wrapping around the cardboard. Try to cross the yarn so as to make small, medium, and large shapes in an interesting way. Do the same with the other two pieces of yarn. If you are not pleased with the first design, remove the yarn and try again.

Now begin adding color with crayons. Try to use a color scheme (three, four, or five colors that go well together) and color only those shapes and spaces needed to make an interesting design. Care must be taken in coloring, for the yarn will move when touched. Turn the cardboard over and color a design on the back. Cut off all loose yarn ends.

Easter Chick Table Decoration

By Amy Chambliss

Draw and cut out the chick pattern shown from a 2½-by-3-inch piece of paper. The base under the chick should be ½ inch deep.

From heavy white construction paper, cut a strip 10 inches long and 3 inches wide. Fold it in half, lengthwise, then in half again, to 2½ by 3 inches. Lay the pattern on it, trace around lightly in pencil, and cut out. Open the strip and decorate on both sides with water colors or crayons.

With three of these strips you can make a six-pointed star around the center bouquet on your Easter table. Place them so the little beaks face out.

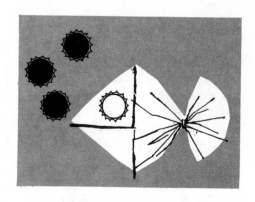

Tin Can Animals
By Mavis Grant

Cute animals may easily be made from assorted sizes of tin cans. Cover the can with construction paper the color of the animal to be made, or use white paper and color it. Paste on construction-paper ears, tails, beaks, and the like. Crayon eyes, feathers, or other lines.

These cans make handy pencil, crayon, or barrette holders.

Fish Picture
By Phyllis Fanders

To make this saucy fish, use a paper bag. Fold over the bottom corners to form a point for the nose. Gather the top and tie it a few inches from the opening. Spread out to form the tail. Paint and decorate as desired. For the eye, use a bottle cap, painted yellow. Paste the fish on blue paper, with bottle-cap bubbles above it.

A Bunny Box   By Virginia Follis

This bunny, filled with colored eggs, makes a nice centerpiece for the table. For an Easter party, he may be filled with small gifts or candy eggs for the guests. Attach each gift to a ribbon leading to a guest's plate.

The body is made from a long box which opens from the top, such as a cracker box, covered with crepe or tissue paper. Cut the paper into strips 2½ inches wide. Fold the strips and fringe them by

cutting 1½-inch slits about ¼ inch apart. Paste the strips to the sides and top of the box, beginning at the bottom and overlapping as shown. On one end of the box, paste a circle of fringe for the tail, with a ball of cotton in the center.

The head is a 9-inch paper plate, fringed around the edge with ¾-

inch slits. For the ears, cut a 6-inch paper plate in half. Curve the cut edges and tips to ear shape. Make slits in the head, slip the ears through from the front, and glue in place on the back of the head. Glue three or four overlapping circles of the fringed paper around the head section as shown, front and back.

The face is a 4-inch circle of plain white paper. Paste it in the center of the head. Cut out and paste on two black paper eyes and a red nose. Make a slit on either side of the nose and insert three blue pipe-cleaner whiskers. Fasten the head to the body with two-pronged paper clips, one through each eye, one through the nose. Cut across the bottom of the paper-plate head on a line with the box bottom.

Basket of Easter Eggs   By Ruth Everding Libbey

Use a long egg carton, one that holds two rows of eggs. Cut off the four cups from one end. Paint them yellow. Cut a narrow strip from the egg carton lid for a handle. Paint it yellow. Glue it to the basket.

Cut apart the eight remaining cups. Trim the edges till the bottom of each one lies flat on the table without wobbling. Glue two cups together to form a make-believe egg. Make four of these. Paint each one a different color or design.

Place the eggs in the basket.

Easter Mobile   By Joyce T. Buckner

Blow out the insides of seven eggs through little holes (one at each end) made by gently tapping the ends with the point of a paring knife. Rinse the shells with water.

Using a long, blunt needle, run a piece of string or yarn through six of the eggshells. The six pieces of yarn should be of different lengths from 7 to 12 inches long. Make a knot in the end of each string small enough to go through the bigger hole in the egg, but large enough so it will not slip through the smaller hole. Paint each egg a different color.

The seventh eggshell should be strung on yarn 18 inches long. This will be the center egg for the mobile, so it should be more highly decorated. An easy way to do this is to use colored ads from an old magazine. Try to find colors that match the colors in the other six eggs. Paste bits of the colored paper to the eggshell, covering it completely.

The frame for the mobile is a piece of cardboard about 1 inch wide and 22 inches long. Paint the cardboard to match the yarn. When the cardboard is completely dry, form the strip into a circle, and staple or paste the ends together.

To hang the mobile, you will need three pieces of yarn 18 inches long. With the needle, make holes in the cardboard ring in three places. Put the yarn through the holes and make knots on the inside of the ring so the yarns cannot pull out.

Tie three of the colored eggs through the same three holes, knotting the strings on the inside of the circle. Between each of these, make three new holes and attach the other three eggshells.

Now you are ready to hang the mobile. Hold up the three hanger yarns on the circle, and the yarn for the center egg. Adjust the hanger yarns so the cardboard frame is level. Adjust the yarn for the center egg so that it hangs just above the other eggs. Knot all four yarns together, and cut off extra yarn. It will take only a thumbtack to hang up the mobile. The slightest breeze will make it move because it is so light.

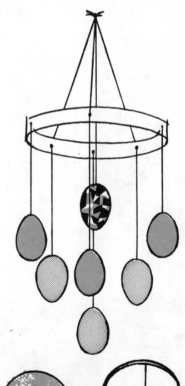

Easter Bonnet Nut Cup   By Ann Hatch

Cut a tiny circle from the center of a gold lace-paper doily 3 to 4 inches in diameter. Make triangular cuts from the circle to the lace edge, as shown. Bend the tabs up toward the right side of the doily.

Cut a strip of colored construction paper 1 by 7 inches. Staple or paste it to the tabs to form the crown. Cut a circle of construction paper a little smaller than the doily. Paste it to the bottom of the doily. Fasten a 1-inch ribbon around the crown. Finish with a bow of baby ribbon where the 1-inch ribbon overlaps. Tuck a few tiny artificial flowers or feathers under the bow.

Bunny Box

By Evelyn Cook

Cut off the top of a milk carton so that a 2-inch-high box is left. Cut a strip of colored paper 2 by 12 inches. Glue it around the box.

Cut a strip of paper 2 by 6 inches. Roll it into cylinder shape for the bunny's head. Fasten it to one side of the box with a two-pronged paper fastener.

Cut two strips of paper 1 by 3 inches. Shape them into rabbit ears and fasten behind the head. Cut eyes, nose, and whiskers from black paper and paste as shown. Finish the face with pink crayon. Paste a tail of cotton on the opposite side of the box. Fill with paper grass and candy eggs. The box can also be used for trinkets.

dle. Stir the wax and pour just a tiny bit into the mold through the enlarged hole. Let this harden to seal the small hole in the bottom of the shell. Then pour in more wax to fill the mold. An egg carton makes a good holder for the mold while you fill it.

Make the wick by dipping a 3-inch piece of string into some of the melted wax. Lay it out straight on newspaper to harden. When the wick is stiff and the wax in the mold is partially set, stick the wick into the candle. Peel off the shell when the candle is hard.

Egg cups make pretty holders for these candles. Or the candles can be flattened slightly on the bottom and set in saucers.

Egg Candles

By Bonnie Leman

Pretty Easter egg candles to decorate your table can easily be made from paraffin and colored crayons.

To make the candle mold, punch a small hole in each end of a raw egg. Blow out the insides. Enlarge the hole in the small end of the shell so it is about the size of a finger tip.

Melt a block of paraffin and a crayon over low heat. Use two crayons for a bright-colored can-

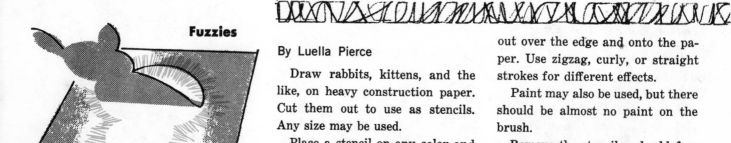

Fuzzies

By Luella Pierce

Draw rabbits, kittens, and the like, on heavy construction paper. Cut them out to use as stencils. Any size may be used.

Place a stencil on any color and size of construction paper desired. Starting in about a half inch on the stencil, bring crayon strokes

out over the edge and onto the paper. Use zigzag, curly, or straight strokes for different effects.

Paint may also be used, but there should be almost no paint on the brush.

Remove the stencil and add features. Pipe cleaners and bits of cotton may be used for whiskers, tails, and ears.

By Dorothe A. Palms

Cut two rabbit head shapes, about 3 by 3½ inches, from light-weight white cardboard. Cut two ears from pink construction paper. Paste the head shapes together, with the ears inserted between them at the top, and a 4-inch white pipe cleaner at the bottom. Paint on black eyes, nose, and mouth. Paste on whiskers and fringed eyebrows cut from black construction paper. Bend the end of the pipe cleaner into a circle and paste it to the top of the body, which is a small box such as gelatin or a pudding mix comes in.

Cut a white facial tissue into eight equal strips, lengthwise. Fold each strip lengthwise and fringe it. Each strip will go around the box once. Start pasting at the bottom. Let the fringe of the next strip overlap the unfringed part of the strip below. Cover the entire box.

Cut two large feet from black construction paper. Paste them to the bottom of the box. Add a bunch of cotton for the tail.

Perky Easter Card

By Frances M. Callahan

Make the folder card from colored construction paper 9 inches long and 4½ inches wide. Fold it crosswise so the top part is about ½ inch shorter, as shown.

Draw and cut out a paper pattern of a bunny head with a bow at the neck. Trace around it on the card, using pink pencil for the head and ears, and blue for the bow. Make pink markings lengthwise in the center of the ears. Glue on sequin eyes. Snip off the side of a sequin to give it a point, and glue in place for the nose.

Cover the bow area with a generous coating of white glue. Cover immediately with tiny colored cake decorations. Then lay the card on a flat surface and pat the decorations gently.

Cover the ears and head in the same way, using minute tapioca that has been sifted through a medium-size-mesh sieve. Do one ear at a time, then the face, keeping carefully within the pink line and away from the sequins. The whiskers are four 1-inch pieces of coarse white thread. Dip the ends in glue and paste in place. Use a toothpick to flick away any tapioca that sticks in the wrong places.

With colored pencils write "Happy Easter" under the bunny head, and a message or verse, such as

This perky bunny
Comes to say,
"Have a glorious
Easter Day!"

A Basket

By Sister Mary Norma

Cut eight strips of colored construction paper, 17 inches long, 1 inch wide.

Cross them on the bottom side of an 8-inch paper plate. Staple the strips near the edge of the plate. Turn the plate right side up and bend the strips upward at the edge of the plate. Through the strips, weave 1-inch strips of contrasting colors. If the strips are not long enough, staple short ones to them. On the top woven strip, staple at each vertical strip. Use a double strip for the handle.

49

Eggs and Egg Heads

By Dorothy Anderson Burge

All of these eggs are formed over an oval-shaped balloon that has been blown up. Cover the blown-up balloon with strips of brown gummed mailing tape, cut in pieces 8 to 10 inches long. Dip them in water, and wrap them around the balloon. Be sure the gummed side of the tape is away from the balloon, not against it. Completely cover the balloon, making sure that each piece of tape touches or overlaps another piece. If you plan to fill with candies, make the egg extra-strong by wrapping more than one layer of wet tape over the balloon.

Painted Easter Egg

While it is still wet and sticky, cover the gummed tape with bright-colored crepe paper. Pull the paper tightly around the egg, smoothing the wrinkles as much as possible. Fasten down loose edges with paste. Let the egg stand overnight or until completely dry. When dry, break the balloon inside by pushing a pin through the outside layers of paper. Using poster paints, paint the egg with designs. Let one side dry before turning the egg over to paint the other side.

Egg Head

Cover with pink crepe paper, and paint on the face and hair. Make one egg for each member of the family. Try to make each face look like the person it represents. Tape a bow of crepe paper under the chin.

Fluffy Egg

Cut ten to fifteen strips of colored crepe paper, about 1 inch wide and 20 inches long. Fringe by making scissor cuts ½ to ¾ inches deep along one edge of the strip. While the tape is still wet and sticky, cover it with rows of the fringed strips. Start each strip at the end of the one before it. Stick the unfringed side to the egg, and fluff the fringes up. When it is completely dry, break the inside balloon. Decorate with odd bits of artificial flowers, leaves, and pieces of ribbon.

Bunny Head

Use three balloons, one oval or pear-shaped for the head, and two long, narrow ones for the ears.

Follow instructions for making either the egg head or the fluffy egg, depending on whether you want a smooth or fluffy bunny. When the head is dry, paint on nose, eyes, and mouth with poster paints. Use straws from a broom for whiskers, pushing them gently through the crepe paper. Tape a crepe paper bow to the neck.

Candy Containers

Cut a small, round circle in the back of the finished egg. Gently stuff it with cellophane straw and small candies or jelly beans. Cover the hole with clear plastic.

Easter Shapes Into Easter Designs

By Lee Lindeman

A simple egg pattern, a rabbit pattern, or a chick pattern can be used to make pleasing designs.

Cut one of these patterns from a piece of paper. Place it on a larger piece of paper and draw around it. Place the pattern next to the one you drew, and draw around it again. Repeat this until the whole paper is covered. You may want to repeat this procedure with some overlapping. Or you may want to make a picture with the pattern. For example, from an egg pattern you could form a rabbit or a chick.

You can color your design with paint, crayons, chalk, dry marker, ink, or even colored pencil. Try a few designs and see what you can create.

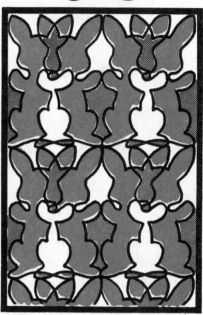

51

Pick a Cork
By Lee Lindeman

Round wood or plastic toothpicks and corks can be made into attractive mobiles or ornaments.

With a needle or pin, make holes in the cork and then carefully stick toothpicks into the cork in different arrangements. Long toothpicks can be broken into small pieces and used to make a more interesting design. Make a star or a spider or a satellite or any interesting arrangement.

When you have finished arranging the toothpicks, tie a long piece of string to the cork. Hold the string as you dip your cork creation into your favorite color paint. If you wish, you can spray your creation instead of dipping it. Place it on a piece of wax paper to dry.

Clothespin Animals
By June Rose Mobly

The materials needed are pipe cleaners, clothespins, cardboard, and poster paint.

Fly

Cut out and paint the cardboard wing piece. Attach by means of pipe cleaner to a clothespin which has been painted black. Use pieces of pipe cleaner twisted around the clothespin to form the three pairs of legs.

Rabbit

The prongs of one clothespin form the long ears. Tie together two clothespins so that one is in the position of a rabbit's head. Add pipe cleaner legs and cotton tail. Paint facial features and body color.

Mouse

Paint the clothespin body black. Make the head from paper rolled into a cone. Cut the open end to include ears as shown. Paint on the eyes, nose, and whiskers. Use pipe cleaner to fasten it to the body, and to form legs and tail.

Place Markers
By Texie Hering

These markers are made from discarded plastic containers. Draw and cut out paper patterns of pony, cow, and puppy faces, and a "neck" for each, as illustrated. Trace around them on the plastic container and cut out. Tie a colored string halter to each neck. Draw eyes on each face. Staple the faces to the necks through the eyeholes. Paint on the features, preferably with enamel or oil paint.

Double Features

By Ella L. Langenberg

It is fun to cut things as double features. Just follow these simple directions.

Use thin paper. The cutouts illustrated were made from 3-by-5-inch pieces, but any size will do. Bring the short ends together and fold, then fold again. Draw half of the figure on the fold. Cut out, leaving the part on the fold uncut. When opened, the two figures will be joined together, and will be alike on both sides.

In the same way, try cutting other shapes suggesting holidays.

To cut shapes which are not alike on both sides, fold the paper only once. Draw the full figure with some part of it touching on the folded edge of the paper.

There are many ways to use these cutouts—greeting cards, place cards, table decorations. Even room decorations can be made by pasting the cutouts together to form long rows, or cutting them from long strips of paper, properly folded.

Egg Head Characters

By Dorothy R. Appleton

Egg head characters can be made any time of the year. However, why not practice making a few and be ready to surprise friends and relatives?

The egg must be very gently tapped at both ends with a nail or any pointed object and a light hammer. Blow out the contents and save for cooking.

Sketch a face on the shell with pencil, then with India ink. Ears and nose may be cut from paper.

The stand may be made with lightweight cardboard or colored construction paper. Cement or glue the egg to the stand before decorating. It gives you something to hold while working.

Paint with water colors or tempera. Glue on paper ears and nose. Ribbons, feathers, fur, and the like, used with imagination, aid in decorating the characters.

Try a few to get the feel of it, and you will find yourself searching for characters to make.

Paper Fishbowl

By Frances Benson

Fold a piece of transparent waxed paper (not the kind with the milky look). Cut out a fishbowl shape with the bottom of the bowl on the fold.

Cut green paper to look like water plants. Cut goldfish from orange paper. Draw the eyes and gills, and a few scales, on both sides of each fish.

Place the fish between the two layers of the bowl with the plants at the bottom. Press the bowl lightly with a warm iron to seal in place.

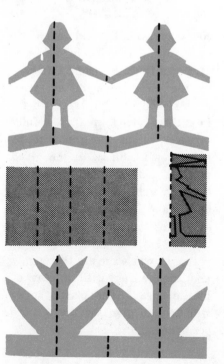

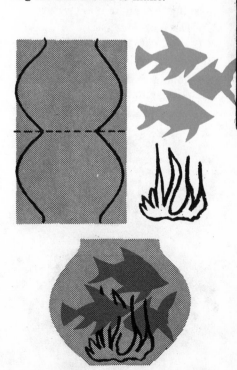

53

Gifts for Mother

By Lee Lindeman

Dressing Table Trays

Your mother, sister, aunt, or grandmother would like to have one of these beautiful trays on her dressing table. It can be used for bobby pins, ribbons, combs, brushes, or even jewelry. These trays are made from clean cardboard trays on which fruit and vegetables come from the grocery store. Ask your mother to save the trays for you.

Paint the cardboard tray your favorite color. Trim the edge with lace, sequins, silk cord, braid, rickrack, or small flowers. The trimming should be glued on very carefully and neatly.

Stone Paperweights

Find a smooth stone about the size of your fist. Wash and dry the stone.

Paint a face or animal or design on the stone with poster paint, a marking pen, India ink, or crayons. Use three or four colors.

If you use India ink or paint, let it dry thoroughly. You can give the stone a more permanent finish by shellacking it or spraying it with clear plastic lacquer.

Hot Dish Mats

Hot dish mats are useful as well as beautiful gifts. To make one you will need the following materials: a thin piece of wood, Masonite board, or beaver board, cut to the desired size; clear-drying glue; colored fine gravel from a craft shop or a pet store; heavy cord or string. You will need gravel in two or three colors.

On a piece of paper draw several designs that you think would be good for a hot dish tile. Keep your design large and simple. Choose the best design and draw it on the tile.

Pour some glue along one of the drawn lines and carefully place string along the glued line. Press the string down gently. Repeat this until all lines have a string glued to them. Glue a border of string around the surface of the whole tile.

You are now ready to use the

colored gravel. Use only one color at a time and work in only one area at a time. Spread a thin coat of the clear glue in an area. Sprinkle on enough gravel to fill in all the glued area. Carefully press down on the gravel to be sure it will adhere to the glued surface. Let this dry. When dry, carefully shake off the excess gravel and save it. Continue the same procedure with each area and color.

Let the whole tile dry thoroughly and then spray with a coat of plastic spray. The plastic spray will help to give the tile a more permanent finish.

54

Stone Pendant

Find a small stone—one that is nicely shaped and with a beautiful color. Wax or shellac the stone to bring out more of the natural colors.

Wind a 6-inch piece of bendable wire around the stone. Wrap enough wire around the stone to secure it, but leave some of the stone visible on all sides.

When you have just about used up the wire, make a small loop in the end of the wire. Twist the loop a few times. A pair of small round-nose pliers are good for bending and twisting the loop.

This stone pendant can be hung on a chain for a necklace, or on a key chain or bracelet.

Beads of Clay

Using the kind of clay that is very hard when dried, roll small pieces of clay into balls or other desired shapes. While the clay is still moist, take a round toothpick and carefully make a hole through the center of each bead. Remove the toothpick and let the clay beads dry.

When the beads are hard and dry, paint them with poster paint. Choose any color or combination of colors you like. For a permanent finish, spray the beads with a clear plastic spray after the color is dry.

Use strong button thread for stringing the beads.

This makes a nice gift for your mother, grandmother, or sister.

Earrings From Clay

These earrings are fun and easy to make. You will need the following materials: a small amount of self-hardening clay, a pair of earring backs, clear shellac or clear plastic spray, poster paint and a fine brush, and creamy white glue that dries clear.

Form a small shape from the clay. It can be a flower shape, a star shape, a small square, or any shape you think suitable for earrings. Be sure to make two earrings that are exactly alike—one for each ear. Let the clay shapes dry thoroughly.

Paint with poster paint. They can be painted with a pretty pastel color or even with gold paint. Allow paint to dry.

Coat the painted clay with a clear shellac or plastic spray. Clear nail polish could also be used. Coat several times for a high shine and let dry completely.

Use the glue to attach the earring backs in place on the painted clay forms.

Tissue Paper Flowers

Tissue paper flowers are pretty and very easy to make. Use colored tissue paper for the blossoms and the leaves. The stems are made from pipe cleaners.

Place several pieces of tissue paper together so that you have four or five layers. Cut out a small circle from the layers of tissue. The circle should be about 3 inches across. Fold the circle in half and then into quarters. Scallop the top edge; do not cut the point at the bottom. Open the tissue circles and smooth flat. Pull up and pinch the center of the tissue circles that are piled on top of each other, and carefully fluff the petals.

Attach the pinched part of the flower to a pipe cleaner with cellophane tape, string, thread or very fine wire.

Cut out the leaves from tissue paper. Glue to the stem. The leaves can also be made from poster or construction paper.

Unusual Gifts   By Jeanne Gladstone

Old greeting cards or colored pictures from old catalogs can be used to make pretty candy dishes, cover old lamp bases, and make plain bottles into fancy ones.

From cardboard cut an equal-sided triangle, a half inch to an inch, depending on the size of the object to be covered. Use this as a pattern to cut the cards or pictures into triangles. Then start to glue them on in any direction, up or down. Just make sure they entirely cover the object you are working on. Some of them will have to overlap each other to accomplish this.

Let the glue dry for about 24 hours. Then put a coat of clear shellac over the entire surface.

Mother's Day Card

By Katherine Corliss Bartow

Cut out three flowers from colored paper, each a little smaller than the other; the largest about 2½ inches wide. Paste on cotton centers colored with yellow chalk. Cut the flowerpot from red construction paper.

The card is white or cream construction paper, 12 inches long and 6½ inches wide. Measure down 2⅝ inches from the top and fold the paper forward. Fold this forward twice more.

Unfold the paper. Glue the flowerpot at the bottom left and ink in the markings. At the top left, paste the largest flower. With green pencil or crayon, draw a stem connecting pot and flower. Draw and color the leaves.

Fold down the top section, paste on the middle-sized flower, and draw leaves and stem, connecting the stem with the one from the flowerpot. Fold down again, and repeat this process. At the right of this flower, print "My love for you just grows." Unfold and print "and grows." Unfold again and print "and GROWS."

At the left of the pot, print "Happy Mother's Day."

Flamingo or Stork

By Hilda K. Watkins

In the corner of a large envelope draw and cut out the body shape shown. Cut slits to form wing feathers.

Twist two pipe cleaners together to form one long piece. Run it through holes punched in the body. Bend it down the sides of the body for legs. Clip a spring-type clothespin at the end of each leg, then bend pipe cleaner so the bird will stand.

Use pink paint for a flamingo, or black for a stork. Open the folded neck and bend into shape.

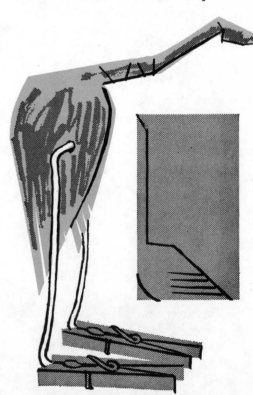

1

2

3

4

May Basket   By Bernice Walz

Cut a four-hole section from an egg carton. Trim the edges neatly. Cut a piece of aluminum foil large enough to cover the bottom and sides of the basket. Fold over the top edges and press into place, trimming off any excess. Insert a green pipe cleaner through the center and twist the ends together to make a loop handle. Tie a yellow ribbon bow on the handle where it is joined together. Put a few artificial or real flowers into the center. Fill the four sections with small candies or popcorn.

Jewelry Box   By Dorothe A. Palms

A cigar box covered with a self-adhering decorator plastic makes an attractive jewelry box.

Cover each of the ends first. Let each piece extend about a half inch over all four sides.

The piece for the front should extend over top and bottom, but be even with the sides.

The lid top and the back of the box are covered with one piece which extends over the sides of the lid, but is even at the sides of the back. Close the lid while extending the piece down the back and over the edge of the bottom, so the lid will open and close easily.

The bottom is covered with a piece that fits evenly on all sides.

Fold a 3-inch piece of ribbon in half, and glue to the underside of the lid. Then cover the inside of the lid. This piece fits evenly on three sides, but extends down into the inside of the box.

Decorate the top with cloth tape or colored ink marker, or leave it plain.

Papier-mache Hand Puppet   By Tera Burgundy

To make the papier-mache, cut several sheets of newspaper into 1-inch squares. Put them in a large pan, pour just enough boiling water on top to cover, and let them soak overnight. Ask Mother to help with this.

Squeeze the wet newspaper into a pulp with your hands. Measure out one cup of the mixture and place on wax paper. Add two tablespoons of flour paste, and mix thoroughly. The mixture should be soft and pliable like modeling clay.

Blow up a balloon about the size of a tennis ball. Knot the end. For the neck, cut off 1¼ inches from a cardboard tube. Tie this to the balloon with string, as shown.

Now shape the newspaper mixture around the balloon, about ¼ inch thick. Start at the top and work down. Put on a nose and add some ears to suit whatever character you choose. Rub the surface smooth with your fingers as you work. Then put it aside to dry overnight.

Puncture the balloon and remove it from the inside. Be sure the papier-mache is thoroughly dry before painting with tempera paints or water colors. Apply a coat of shellac when the paint is dry.

Make a cloth body. Add felt hands. Leave an opening at the neck. Glue a piece of felt to the neck of the finished puppet head. Then sew the cloth body securely in place.

57

Bandanna Handkerchief Apron

By Doris P. Wilson

Two red and two blue figured bandanna handkerchiefs combine to make a gay apron for barbecues or parties.

Arrange three of the handkerchiefs together with one red one in the center, and a blue one on each side of it. Stitch them together on the wrong side, with ½-inch seams. Along the top, run a gathering stitch about ½ inch down from the edge. This can be done by hand or on a sewing machine, using longest stitch. Leave ample thread length for pulling up gathers.

For the waistband and ties, cut the fourth handkerchief into three equal parts. Sew them together to make a long strip. The middle section is the waistband; the other two are the ties. Sew narrow hems along the edges of the two tie pieces.

Fold waistband in half lengthwise. Fold under the raw edges and press. Pull up the gathers in the apron piece to fit the waistband. Insert it between the folded waistband and sew in place. Since the handkerchiefs are already hemmed, no other hemming is required.

Some Things To Make

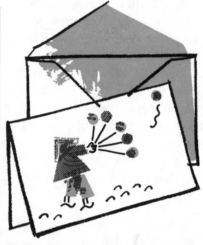

All-occasions Greeting Card

By Helen C. Gillingham

Use cancelled stamps of many colors. Cut the figure out of three stamps and paste to a blank correspondence card or a piece of construction paper the size of the envelope you wish to use.

Cut out tiny circles for the balloons, or punch them out with a paper punch. An easy way to paste these on is to squeeze on tiny spots of glue first, then dampen a pinhead to pick up the little balloons and put them in place.

Draw a curvy line for the one that got away! Draw in the two short lines for each leg, curved lines for shoes, and tiny curved lines for the cobbled street. With a pen or pencil crayon you can also draw a small hand and the strings attached to the balloons.

Coaster

By De Laine Squires

To make this attractive coaster, use four pieces of 3-by-5-inch cardboard like the sides of cereal boxes; two pieces of paper-backed foil; and a cutout. The coaster may be any shape desired.

Glue two of the cardboard pieces together and press under a heavy weight. Do the same with the other two pieces. Measure and cut off all corners to match.

Thoroughly coat one side of each cardboard with glue, and cover with the foil. Fold the corners back first, then the sides and ends. Smooth out any wrinkles in the foil with a soft cloth. Fold the extra foil to the back and glue firmly.

To make the coaster solid, glue a small piece of cardboard to the center back of one cardboard piece. Then glue the two pieces together, matching corners. Press the coaster for several hours. Decorate one side with a cutout.

58

Knitting Box

By Erma E. Gothro

Use a cylindrical box with a cover, such as an oatmeal box. Cover it with wallpaper or construction paper, or paint it with tempera or finger paints. Decorate a plain color with painted designs. Give it a coat of shellac. Make the cover to match.

For the handle, use a piece of rug yarn or other heavy string of the desired length. Punch holes opposite each other, 1½ inches down from the top of the box. Insert the two ends of the handle, and tie them in a large knot to make the handle secure.

Glitter Name Designs

By Bernice Walz

Fold white, colored, or gold-sprayed paper, lengthwise. Along the inside fold line, write "Mother" or a person's first name to fit the space, using thin, quick-drying glue. Press the paper together to blot. Open and shake the desired color of glitter on the glue. Allow it to dry thoroughly. Mount it on paper of contrasting color.

These designs can be used as greeting cards or to decorate packages.

A Mother's Day Corsage

By Dorothe A. Palms

Materials needed are one sheet of construction paper, any pastel color; eight 6-inch green pipe cleaners; four small plastic bottle tops or caps from toothpaste tubes; two green leaves, artificial or cut from heavy construction paper; one yard of white ribbon about ¾ inch wide.

For the paper flowers, cut four pieces, 3 by 5 inches. Fold them in half to 1½ by 5 inches. Glue the 5-inch sides together at the edge only. Working along the folded side, cut slits 1 inch deep and about 1/16 inch apart. Brush on a ½-inch-wide strip of glue along the 5-inch uncut side. Place a pipe cleaner into the glue at the end of the strips as shown, and roll the strip around it tightly. When the glue is dry, press the flowers open.

For the cap flowers, punch a small hole in the cap top. Run a pipe cleaner through it, coil the end, and push the cap up tight against the coil. Make four of these flowers.

Arrange the eight flowers into a corsage as shown, twisting the stems together. Attach the leaves at the back. Fasten the ribbon bow below the flowers.

Clown Doorstop

By Joyce T. Buckner

Make arms from rolled paper. Attach them to a round cleanser can with household cement or glue. Paint the entire can and arms with paint. Allow to dry. It may take two coats to cover the printing.

Fill the can with dry sand or fine dirt by funneling it into the holes in the lid. Put masking tape over the holes except the center one. Into the center hole insert the stick of a lollipop. Tape around the hole to keep the sand from sifting out.

Crumple newspaper around the lollipop to make the head larger. Double a half-sheet of tissue paper and put it over the crumpled newspaper to make the head. Secure it with a rubber band. Trim the tissue paper to make a collar around the clown's neck. Paint a face on the clown, mark his legs, and decorate his body as you like. Make a hat from colored paper, and glue in place.

Sailors, soldiers, policemen, and many other persons could be made in the same way.

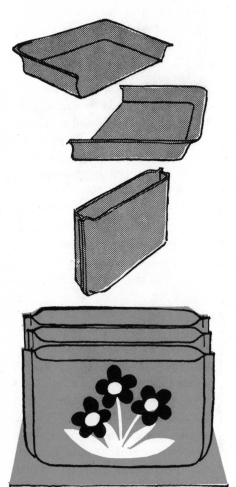

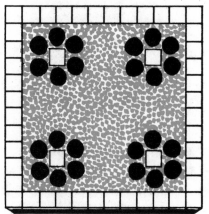

Mosaic Tile Hot Plate

By Lee Lindeman

You will need the following materials to make this mosaic tile hot plate: a piece of fiberboard or thin plywood about 6 inches square; small pieces of tile from a hardware store or hobby shop; colored gravel; and creamy white clear-drying glue.

Using the thin board as a base, arrange a pleasing border with the small tile pieces, and glue them to the board. Use more small tiles to form a design in the center. Glue to the board. Let the tiles dry thoroughly.

In the empty places spread a thin layer of creamy white glue. While the glue is still moist, pour some colored gravel over it. Press the gravel down carefully. Again let the tile dry thoroughly.

This makes a decorative and useful gift.

Breakfast Napkin Holder

By Lee Lindeman

This is an easy and useful Mother's Day gift to make. Save three molded paper trays in which meat comes from the store. Wash the trays quickly, and let them dry.

Carefully cut a tray in half. Glue the two halves to each other, forming a pocket. Repeat this with the other two trays. Glue the three pockets side by side. The napkin holder will stand by itself. Or you can glue it to a cardboard base.

Paint the holder with poster paint. When the paint has dried, decorate with colorful cut paper designs. You could also paint on some very attractive designs. Now add some paper napkins to your new holder.

A Pet To Carry By Texie Hering

Bend a pipe cleaner into the shape shown in Figure 1. Tie with thread to hold in place. Attach yarn ½ inch from end of tail. Wind around pipe cleaner to end of tail and then back to body. Fasten. Using a darning needle, weave the yarn up and down between the pipe cleaner to cover back legs, body, front legs, head, and ears.

Pull yarn under weaving and snip off. Add sequin or bead eyes and a felt collar.

If desired, elastic thread can be attached to the end of the collar and then to the body so the pet can be worn on the arm. The pet can also be bent to stand by itself as shown in Figure 2.

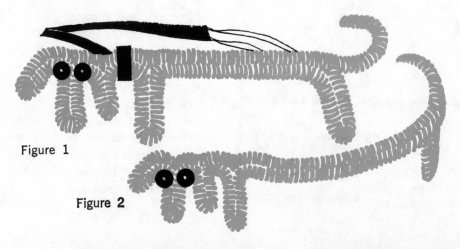

Figure 1

Figure 2

A Hat for Little Girls

By Velma Colvin

For the hat, use cardboard from a dress box, or two layers of stiff paper. Cut a circle 9 inches across. Draw and cut out six flowers. Color them on both sides. Arrange them around the brim, on the topside of the hat, and staple them in place. Make two 1-inch slits, each slit about an inch from the center of the hat. Slip a piece of ribbon through the slits, bringing the two ends to the underside of the brim. The ribbon must be long enough to tie under the chin.

Small hats for dolls may be made in the same way.

Rustic Wooden Earrings

By Lee Lindeman

Find a branch that is about an inch thick. Remove the bark. Saw off two pieces, each about ¼ inch thick. Sand the rough sides until they feel very smooth. Coat with lacquer or clear nail polish. Place on a piece of foil or waxed paper, and let dry.

Glue the finished wooden discs to earring backs. After drying for one day, the earrings are ready to give as a gift.

A Rose Petal Card for Mother's Day

By Beatrice Bachrach

Select a rose that is about to wither. Press the petals between the pages of a heavy book for a few days; also press the leaves. Put white glue on the card in the area where the rose petals are to be placed. Put the petals in the glue. Draw a graceful stem. Apply glue for placement of leaves. A dab of glitter in the center of the flower and along the stem dresses up the card.

Cotton-ball Mother's Day Cards

By Beatrice Bachrach

Draw a flower arrangement on the card front. Place dabs of glue, and put cotton balls onto the glue. The flower centers may be scraps of cloth, colored paper, or a button. Add stems and leaves with paint or crayon.

A Tulip for Mom

By Beatrice Bachrach

Draw a tulip on construction paper. On each side add a long strip. Cut out. Bend the strips to form a circle, and paste the ends together. Cut out green paper stem and leaves. Paste the stem to the bottom inside front of the tulip. Fold a piece of construction paper in half for a card. Cut to desired size with pinking shears, or the edges can be left plain. Paste the back center of the circle and the bottom of the stem to the card. Write a message on the inside. If desired, the card can be pasted to a larger piece of construction paper of a different color.

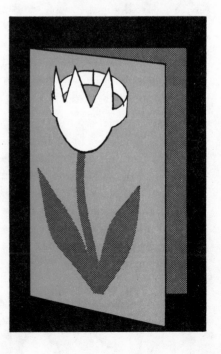

By June Rose Mobly

Most of these animals are made entirely from paper drinking cups which have double handles of light-weight cardboard. Egg carton cups and pointed drinking cups are used for a few parts. Each section is shaped with scissors. Sections are then fastened together with pipe cleaner run through holes punched in the paper, the ends being bent flat or twisted. Poster paint is used for body color, markings, and facial features. The illustrations are a guide for cutting, but the choice of colors is yours.

Frog

The bottom of a paper cup is bent in half to form the frog head with a large, slightly open mouth. The body-leg section of the frog is fashioned from a cup handle. Pipe cleaner is used for the neck and as a support between the front legs. Paint large round eyes.

Lobster

A cup handle is cut to form the lobster's front claws. To this piece is fastened the tail section which is cut from the sidewall of the cup. Pipe cleaner legs and antennae are twisted into place before the entire lobster is painted. Add the eyes and body markings.

Mouse

The head of this mouse is cut as one piece from a cone-shaped drinking cup. The body-legs section is made from a cup handle, and the long tail is the rim of a paper cup. All three sections are fastened together with pieces of pipe cleaner. You may paint your mouse or leave him white.

Monkey

The monkey body, arms, and legs are cut in one piece from the handle of a cup. Add to this a long pipe cleaner tail and a head cut from a piece of egg carton.

Octopus

The handles from four paper cups are used to make the eight legs of the octopus. Cut each handle so that the pair of legs is connected at the top only. Using pipe cleaner, join the pairs of legs to each other and to a head cut from sidewall material. Color and add features.

Grasshopper

For the head hold the handle against the sidewall of the cup and cut around the handle. Bend and fasten with pipe cleaner as shown in the illustration. Each wing is cut from sidewall material and is fastened to the head section by one end of a pipe cleaner. The rest of this pipe cleaner is bent into a long hind leg. The middle and front legs, and the antennae are also pipe cleaner. Paint and decorate the grasshopper.

Cat

Join the handles of two drinking cups to form the body of the cat. The bottom of a cup is used for the head, two points of sidewall material being left on for the ears. Use pipe cleaner to fasten the parts together, and to form a long tail. Paint the cat any color you wish.

Turtle

The shell, legs, and tail of the turtle are cut in a single piece from the bottom portion of a paper cup. For the head, cut the handle from a cup. Remove the center connecting part of the handle so you have two pieces. Join these together with a piece of sidewall material to fill in the hole. Fasten the head to the body. Paint as desired.

Duck

For the body, hold the handle against the sidewall of the cup and cut around the handle. Bend and fasten with pipe cleaner as illustrated. Add pipe cleaner legs and a head cut from another handle.

Dog

The handles from two drinking cups are needed for this dog. One handle is used for the head section and the other for the body-leg section. Connect the two with a pipe cleaner neck and add a pipe cleaner tail. Paint as desired.

Penguin

The handle of a paper cup is cut to form the body-wings-feet section of the penguin. The head is cut from the bottom of the cup. The bill is the pointed tip of a cone-shaped drinking cup. Paint after all parts are fastened together with pipe cleaner.

Kangaroo

This kangaroo is made in four sections: the head, the front-legs section, the hind-legs-body section, and the tail. All are fashioned from cup handles except the head which is cut from sidewall material of a cup. Join all sections together with pipe cleaner, and paint.

Elephant

Cut both the handle and sidewall material so that the handle forms the four legs and the sidewall material forms the stomach. The head-trunk section is cut from a second cup with the middle support of the handle forming the head and the curved section of the handle forming the trunk. Ears cut from sidewall material are fitted through a slit in the head. Pipe cleaner is used for the tail, to fasten the head to the body, and underneath the body from one side to the other as a support. Apply poster paint as the last step.

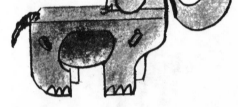

Skunk

Cut the handle from a paper cup. Bring it together and fasten with pipe cleaner. To this body section add a tail and a head, both cut from a second handle. Paint to resemble a skunk.

Y E A R   R O U N D

Swan

By Phyllis Fanders

Cut six pieces of heavy white paper the shape of a teardrop as in Figure 1. Lay these in an even pile and sew together down the center from top to bottom. Glue the bottom one to a cardboard of the same shape.

Using just a bit of glue, fasten each piece to the next one at alternate points as in Figure 2.

Add a pipe cleaner neck and a paper head.

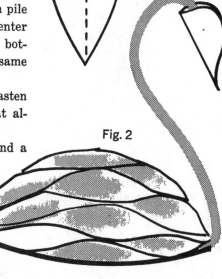

Fig. 1

Fig. 2

Totem Pole

By Phyllis Fanders

Paint a group of spools different colors. Stack and glue them together, inserting paper hands between the spools.

Paint faces on each spool. Glue a bottle cap on the very top.

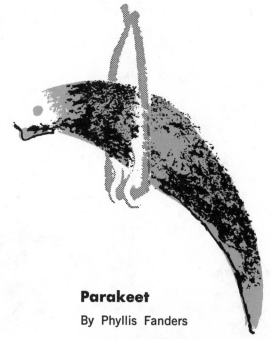

Parakeet

By Phyllis Fanders

Select a milkweed pod that has lost its seeds, but is not too dry. Paint with poster paint to resemble a parakeet. Paint the stem yellow for the beak and add two dots for eyes. Insert a length of yellow pipe cleaner through the body, and bend to form the legs.

Make a pipe-cleaner perch. Fasten the parakeet to it by the claws.

Pencil Caddy

By Hilda K. Watkins

A handy pencil holder may be made from any empty box with a pouring spout. Make it to look like a bulldog or bullfrog.

Use the upper 3½ inches of the box. Cut a triangular piece out of each side as shown by the shaded area.

Bend down the top of the box along the dotted line to form the back of the animal. Cut off the end. Fasten the top and sides together with gummed tape.

For the frog, paste green construction paper over the back, sides, and face. Cut out the front and sides of the body to make crooked front legs. Draw the back legs, feet, eyes, nose, and markings with black ink or crayon.

For the dog, cover the back, sides, and face with white paper. With colored crayon or ink make the eyes, nose, and spots. Paste on two floppy ears and a red tongue.

The spout or mouth will hold pens or pencils.

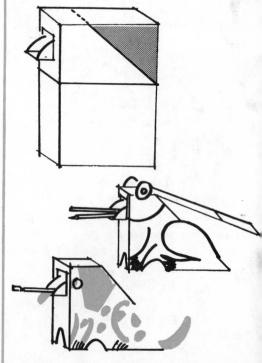

64

Transparencies From Autumn Foliage

By Deirdre B. Watkins

Make a collection of fresh, newly fallen leaves. Look for unusual colors, mottling, streaks, speckles, or the lacy skeleton remains. Ferns, feathery foliage, and milkweed seeds are also good. Use materials that will lie fairly flat.

Cover the ironing board with a layer or two of old cloth or heavy paper—NOT newspaper. Set the iron for medium hot or "wool."

Fold in half a piece of waxed paper that is double the length the finished transparency will be. Unfold it, and place a paper drinking straw along the fold. Arrange the design of leaves on the bottom half. Carefully lower the top half, keeping the straw in the fold, and iron over the whole piece. Work from the center out, trying not to disturb the arrangement. If a leaf does get out of place, peel the paper back gently, replace the leaf, and repeat the sealing process. Be sure to seal the edges well. Trim if necessary.

Run string or yarn through the straw, and hang your picture in a window.

Try different effects and color schemes. For windows with small panes, omit the straw, and tape the transparency to the sash.

For a rustic picture frame, cut four straight twigs or branches a little longer than the paper, tie them together with dark thread to form a rectangle with corners overlapping. Tape the picture to the back.

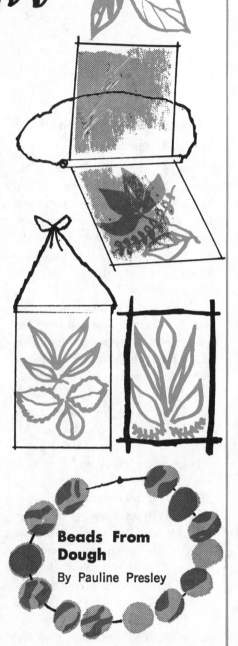

Beads From Dough

By Pauline Presley

Roll a bit of dough between the palms into the desired bead shape. Feel free to mix different colors together for a pretty, mottled effect. While the dough is soft, string the beads with a large needle and double thread. The beads will harden as they dry.

Dough may be purchased; or may be made by mixing 3 cups of flour, 2 cups of salt, 1 cup of water, and a tablespoon of salad oil.

A Scarecrow

By Velma Colvin

Use four cardboard tubes from toilet tissue for the arms and legs, and a longer tube from waxed paper for the body. Cut the long tube in proportion to the arms and legs. Roll a short cardboard tube for the head. Fasten the arms, legs, and head to the body with two-pronged paper fasteners as shown.

Color the scarecrow with tempera paint or crayon. Paint eyes, nose, and mouth on the face.

Make a hat from colored paper. Cut pieces of old bright-colored cloth for the clothes, and drape them over the body. Push long pieces of dried grass or straw into the arms, legs, and head, allowing some to stick out. Bend straw around the neck and put the hat on.

If the scarecrow is to stand up, work with the straw coming out of the legs until the scarecrow is balanced right. If the scarecrow is to be hung up as a decoration, punch a hole in the back of the head, and loop a string through it.

Peanut Clown Marionette
By David Weiman

Use two or three peanuts for the clown's body, two for each arm and leg, a small one for each hand and foot, and a large one for the head. String them together with needle and thread. Be sure to make big knots at the end of the thread so the peanuts will not slip off.

Using poster paint or water colors, paint the clown white. Then paint green stripes over his body. Make his feet black and his hands yellow. Give him a smiling red mouth, and a red nose and cheeks. Use black paint for his eyes and ears, and paint a blue cap on his head.

Now add strings and a control stick to make the clown into a performing marionette. Glue two Popsicle sticks together to form a T. Attach black thread from the knees of the clown and to each end of the T, as shown. Now glue another Popsicle stick across the center of the T. Attach threads from the clown's hands to the ends of this stick. The control stick should now look like a T that has been crossed twice: once across the top, and again halfway down the middle.

To make the clown dance and jump, hold the control stick in one hand and pull the strings with the other hand.

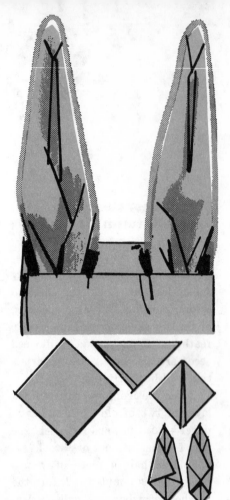

Cap With Donkey Ears
By Ruth Everding Libbey

Use a brown paper bag that will fit over your head. Cut the bag off to about 6 inches in length. Fold the open end up about 2 inches all around, then once again, to form a good firm band.

To make the ears, cut two pieces about 14 inches square from a paper bag. Fold each square in half diagonally. Bring the two bottom points of this triangle up to the top point, and crease. Turn this square upside down and fold in the side points to make an ear shape. Tie with twine. Slip each ear into the foot of an old nylon stocking. Put glue around the bottoms and insert them in the band of the cap. Hold in place with clips till the glue is dry.

Cut a slit inside the band on each side and insert a long ribbon tie.

Paper Party Baskets

By Deirdre B. Watkins

Make a sample basket first. Cut an 8-inch square of stiff paper. Fold it in half twice, corner to corner. Open it, then fold all four corners in to meet exactly in the center. Flip this over, and again fold the four corners to the center, creasing the folds well. Fold this in half twice so you have a small, flat square. Crease well.

Now open this square just enough to get your thumb and fingers in under the four top flaps, and pinch the center part together so you have a four-section basket resting on four neat little points.

These baskets can be used as candy or nut cups at a party. Make them from colored construction paper, bright foil wrapping paper, or glazed colored shelf paper. Decorate with picture cutouts, sequins, rickrack, lace, or whatever scraps you have on hand.

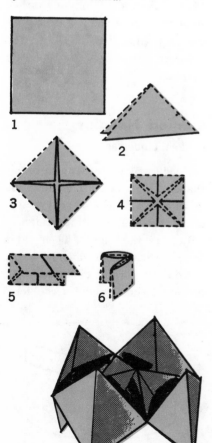

Beach Pails
From Plastic Containers

By Ruth Dougherty

Use an empty plastic bleach container, either half-gallon or gallon size. Cut off the top with scissors. (This can be used as a play funnel, just as it is.)

Cut the top of the pail evenly, or scallop. For the handle, use the strip cut off. Fasten it onto the pail with metal paper fasteners. The handle may also be made from

Crayon and Chalk Pictures

By Lee Lindeman

Cover a large piece of paper with brightly colored chalk. Blow off the extra chalk dust into the wastebasket. Apply a heavy coat of light-colored crayon over the chalk. Now put on a heavy layer of black or dark-colored crayon.

Place a sheet of paper over the chalk and crayon paper. Draw a design or picture on this paper using the handle of a spoon, scissors, brush handle, or a pen holder. Press hard as you draw with one of these instruments.

Separate the papers and look at the pictures that you have made. You have two interesting pieces!

cord, plastic lanyard, or rug yarn with wooden or plastic beads strung on it if desired.

Decorate the pail with gay designs or pictures done in bright-colored enamel paints or nail polish. Crayon also works nicely. These pails are especially enjoyable to make for a younger brother or sister.

Colored Rice Picture

By Agnes Choate Wonson

Dip white rice into different colors of tempera paint or water color paint. Let the rice dry thoroughly.

Cut a piece of colored construction paper or cardboard about 3½ by 7½ inches. Use pencil to sketch two long cords with lanterns hanging from them as shown. Fill in the top and bottom of each lantern and draw the broken lines across them with black paint or ink.

Run glue over the penciled cords. Cover them with yarn of a different shade from the background.

Now outline the lanterns and arrange flower decorations on them with the colored rice. When the arrangement and colors look right, glue the rice in place.

Let's Make These

Soda Straw Spider

By Agnes Choate Wonson

Cut the body from corrugated cardboard about 4½ inches long. On the ridged side paste white circle eyes with sequin centers.

For the legs, use four colored soda straws and four colored pipe cleaners. Cut off the straws so they are two inches shorter than the cleaners. Run a cleaner through each straw, bending the extra inch at each end. Then bend each one in half to V-shape. Place one pair of legs inside another, and glue both sets to the underside of the body.

Candle Holders

By Dorothy Anderson Burge

Using scissors, remove the top part of a half-gallon plastic bleach bottle, cutting about ½-inch below the handle. Remove the bottom part of the bottle, cutting about 1½ inches from the bottom. The middle portion of the bottle is not used.

Fit the top portion of the bottle on the bottom portion, attaching with cellophane tape. Cover the entire bottom of the bottle, including the cellophane tape, with felt. Or it may be covered with colored crepe paper. Use a transparent white glue. If crepe paper is used,

Eggshell Pictures

By Alyce G. Bennett

Draw a picture or design on a plain white paper plate. Wash eggshells well with soap, and rinse them. Then dye them the colors you want to use in your picture. Paste the pieces of shell in place with plastic glue.

You may prefer to make a mosaic with small pieces. Large pieces will make flower designs such as tulips. Grass or dried reeds may be used for stems.

When dry, spray with clear lacquer. Attach a hanger to the back of the plate.

you may spray the entire candle holder with a spray paint. Felt should not be sprayed.

Cut out and glue on felt decorations—flowers, circles, squares, rectangles, or bows. Felt letters may also be added to spell out "Happy Birthday" or any other greeting. Sequins and glitter may also be used to decorate.

Insert a candle in the bottle opening.

Canned Noodles

By Lee Lindeman

Noodles come in many different shapes and sizes. They can be glued onto a tin can or heavy cardboard box in interesting designs.

Let dry thoroughly. Then paint or spray with your favorite color.

Noodle-decorated containers can be used to hold candy or cookies.

Curly Caterpillar

By Gladys Emerson

To make this caterpillar, cut a piece of construction paper, approximately 1½ by 18 inches. Green, brown, yellow, or orange are the best colors to use. Round off one end for the head. The tail may be made round or pointed. With crayons make an eye and mouth.

Decorate the body with various colored stripes and dots. Put the same decorations on both sides of the worm. Then fold backward and forward, accordion style. Press folds firmly. A string may be attached to the head so that the worm can be pulled.

Three-dimensional Bouquet

By Katherine Corliss Bartow

From heavy paper cut a large flower pattern as shown. Fold on the dotted lines as indicated. Then bring the sides over the center, and the bottom up over the sides. Cut two flowers from different colors, using the folded pattern.

Open out pattern and cut a third flower from a third color. Mark petals on flowers with crayon or pencil of the same color. Leave areas between the dotted lines blank on the folded flower.

Flowers may be mounted on a sheet of white construction paper or pasted on a greeting card.

For a card, fold in half white drawing or construction paper, 8½ by 5½ inches. Arrange the flowers as illustrated, with the folded third flower on top. Paste the center backs only.

The flower center is a thin piece of yellow sponge or paper. Glue in place on the front extension of the folded flower. Add glitter. Draw green stems and leaves.

Open the folded flower and write a message in the center.

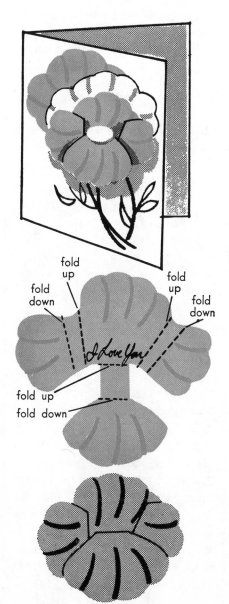

A Flower Basket

By Ellen E. Morrison

This pretty flower basket will hold water to keep flowers fresh. It is made from a square quart-size milk carton.

Measure up about 3 inches from the bottom and cut off evenly all the way around. Punch a small hole in the center of two opposite sides of the cup section, about ¼ inch from the top.

Cut colored crepe paper 3½ inches wide and 24 inches long. Stretch the paper slightly along each edge. With needle and strong thread, make a running stitch along the strip, about 1 inch from the edge. Gather it to 12 inches, or long enough to go around the cup exactly. Sew it to the cup about ½ inch from the top, stitching in and out over the gathering thread. The bottom edge of the paper should be even with the bottom of the cup.

Make a 9-inch handle from wire that will bend easily. Wrap it with crepe paper about 1 inch wide. Bend the wire into a handle shape and fasten the ends into the holes in the sides of the cup.

YEAR ROUND

Cereal Box Train
By Gail Cottingham Koch

Each unit of this train is made from an individual-size cereal box, painted with black and colored enamel. The raised roof of the caboose is the cut-off end of a cereal box, inserted into slits in the caboose top before painting.

The engine smokestack is a thread spool, painted and glued in place. The headlight and other additions to the engine and caboose are metal bottle tops of the press-on type, and need not be painted. The wheels are buttons.

Car names may be painted on, or may be cutouts from magazines.

The train cars are connected with 2-inch heavy twine "couplings" knotted well at each end, with a straight pin run through each knot and then into the car.

Assemble the train and glue it to a 1-inch-wide strip of wood which has been painted black.

Party Hat
By Ella L. Langenberg

Cut a pie-shaped piece out of a paper plate. Lap the rest of the plate over in a tent shape to fit the head. Staple or sew together.

Make a knot in one end of a pipe cleaner. Push the other end of the cleaner through the top of the hat.

For the "antenna," fringe and roll a strip of paper towel, tissue, tablet, or newspaper. Fasten this to the top of the pipe cleaner by twisting the cleaner around it, or by winding thread or a rubber band around it.

Plastic Snowflakes
By Lucile Rosencrans

Use a plastic lid from an ice-cream or food container. Cut off and discard the outer rim. Draw a snowflake design on the remaining circle.

To make a six-pointed snowflake, draw a long narrow X on the circle, then draw a line across the center. This makes six points. Widen the crossed lines as shown. Draw two bars across each line near the outside of the circle. Cut out the snowflake. Glue it on a window or use it as a tree decoration.

Rag Bag Pictures
By Phyllis Fanders

Collect several kinds of scrap materials which Mother has left from her sewing. Cut them into all kinds of shapes—squares, circles, narrow and wide rectangles. Some may even be shaped like raindrops. Arrange these shapes on a piece of construction paper so that they form unusual pictures. Glue them in place with all-purpose glue.

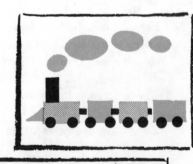

Wall Aquarium

By Dorothe A. Palms

Materials needed are two 9-inch brown paper plates; light-green, dark-green, orange, yellow, and red construction paper; an 8-inch square of clear plastic; colored sand.

Cut out the center of one plate. Lay the rim with the right side up. Glue the plastic over the hole.

Cut a 6-inch circle from light-green construction paper. Glue it to the center of the right side of the other plate. Spread a 1-inch strip of glue across the bottom of the circle. Sprinkle the colored sand over the glue, then shake off any excess. This will look like the bottom of a real aquarium.

Cut two goldfish from the orange paper. Fringe the tails. Glue them, at the middle only, to the center of the plate, bending the heads and tails forward to make the fish look as though they were swimming.

Use the dark-green paper for seaweed, the red paper to make a spiral snail and a starfish, and the yellow paper for tiny sunfish. With black crayon draw a few short wavy lines to look like moving water.

Place the two plates with the right sides together, and staple the rims. Glue a looped-string hanger at the top.

Funny Fruit Faces

By Virginia Appelt

All sorts of fruits can be used to make these faces. Apples, oranges, pears, bananas, peaches, grapefruit, and the like are fine for the heads. Use smaller fruits such as grapes, cherries, raisins, and berries for eyes, nose, and mouth. Slices of apple or sections of orange make good smiling mouths or long noses. Bananas, too, can be sliced to make round eyes.

Try to use many different kinds of fruit to make each face. An apple might have sliced-banana eyes, a raisin nose, and a section of orange for a mouth. A banana might have strawberry eyes, sliced-apple nose, and a plump grape mouth.

To assemble these faces, use short pieces of toothpick. When using round fruit such as grapes and cherries, cut them in half so they will fit better against the surface of the face. Marshmallows can also be used to make little hats.

Vegetable faces for salads can be made in the same manner. Tomatoes, whole peeled cucumbers, whole carrots, and the like can be used for heads. Features can be made from little radishes, strips of celery, carrot, green pepper, lettuce leaves, or any other vegetable which is eaten raw.

These fruit and vegetable faces are lots of fun to eat as well as to make.

A Tiki Mask

By Ruth Everding Libbey

Make this good luck mask out of a piece of brown paper about 20 inches long and 14 inches wide. A heavy paper bag will do nicely.

Draw on it with pencil the outline of a mask similar to the one in the illustration, about 16 inches long and 10 inches wide at its widest part.

Cut slits in the paper all the way around, from the edge of the paper in to the mask outline, as shown in the small drawing. Fold the cut pieces to the back, along the dotted line, overlapping and taping them as you fold. This strengthens the edge of the mask and gives it more weight.

Make the weird black markings with poster paint. Color the mouth red. The eye centers may also be painted red; but if you have two red plastic bottle caps, tape them in place to make even more effective "stand out" eyes. Tape a string hanger to the back of the mask, and hang it on the wall.

You might like to make several of these ferocious-looking masks, using your own designs and colors.

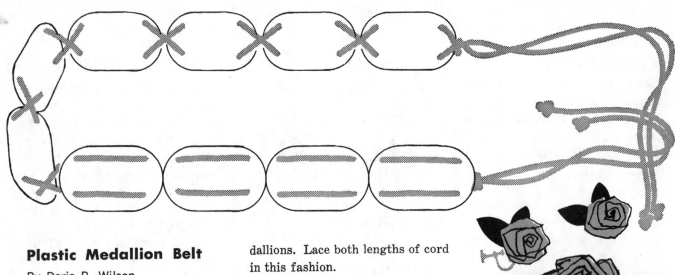

Plastic Medallion Belt

By Doris P. Wilson

Opaque white plastic medallions, cut from bleach or detergent containers and punched with holes for lacing, are assembled on two lengths of white nylon venetian-blind cord to make an unusual tie-on belt. A paper punch or awl is needed for punching the holes.

Cut off the top and bottom of a white plastic bottle, using a knife or scissors. Slit the remaining section and flatten out the plastic.

Cut an oblong paper pattern for the medallion measuring 1½ by 2½ inches. Using scissors, shape into an elongated oval with rounded corners and straight sides. Trace on the plastic. Cut out eight or ten plastic medallions, depending on waist size. With the punch or awl, make two holes in each end of the medallion as shown. Make sure that the upper hole is directly above the lower hole in each pair.

Cut two lengths of the nylon cord long enough to fit around the waist, plus 12 inches for ties.

To lace the medallions on the cord, start at the center back. Add medallions to the right and left as you work. Lace the cord through the right side of the medallion, across the back, forward to the right side again, and down to the opposite hole of the next medallion for crisscross lacings between me-

dallions. Lace both lengths of cord in this fashion.

To hold the medallions in place, sew the lacings together where they cross. The stitches will not show if you work from the back of the belt. Tie knots at each end of the belt assembly and in the ends of the ties.

Egg Carton Train

By Lois Hoadley Dick

The engine is made from a four-cup section of egg carton turned upside down. The wheels are cut from the lid of the carton. The smokestack is a small spool on top of a larger one. Use white glue for pasting. With poster paints, paint the wheels red, the engine blue, and the smokestack yellow.

Other sections may be used for cars, with a single one at the end for a caboose. Also a section may be added with the open side up and filled with pebbles for a coal car.

Flower Earrings and Pin

By Lee Lindeman

Cut a strip of paper toweling 1 by 5 inches. Fold the long way, then open. Apply a thin layer of clear-drying glue on the entire strip. Refold the long way, with the glue on the inside. Roll the strip very tightly for one inch. Then roll loosely, pinching one side of the roll to form a flower shape. Make one flower for each earring and a larger one for the pin. Let them dry until very hard.

Paint the flowers with poster paint, using a small brush to get into the small grooves. When the paint is dry, coat with clear nail polish. Leaves cut from felt may be glued to the bottom of the blossoms if desired. Glue an earring back to each small flower and a safety pin to the larger flower.

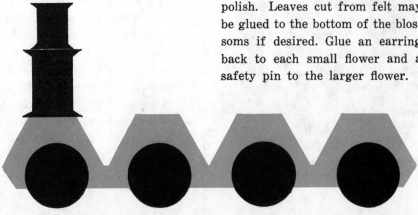

Good-to-eat Favor

By Martha Carpenter

The head is a popcorn ball pressed into a buttered dish or tin to make the round, flat shape. Popcorn that has been mashed into small pieces is easier to shape. Ask Mother for her favorite syrup recipe for holding the popcorn together. Add food coloring to it if you like. Push a lollipop stick into the side before the syrup hardens.

Use candies with a hole in the center for eyes, and gumdrops or other candy for the nose and mouth. Dip them into the syrup, then press them in place. Cover the head and stick with clear cellophane. Gather it below the "chin" and tie it with a ribbon bow.

Butterfly Ornaments

By Dorothy C. Meade

Use metal pouring spouts from salt, detergent, or powdered milk boxes to make butterflies for hair ornaments, pins, or flower arrangements.

Remove spout and hammer it flat. With pointed pliers, bend at an angle which suggests wings. With epoxy glue, attach a bobby pin to make the hair ornament, or a pin back for the brooch, or a long piece of florist's wire for the decoration for a flower arrangement.

The wings may be painted; or covered with cloth to match a favorite dress; or covered with sequins laid on like shingles; or covered with glue, then sprinkled with glitter or beads. Black spots may be made with black ink.

The body is felt cut to shape and glued in place; or florist's wire twisted together and painted black. The head is a knot of thread or wire, with a couple of wire ends left for antennae.

Autumn Leaf Messages

By Ellen E. Morrison

Here is something that will cheer up a sick friend. Cut shapes of autumn leaves out of different colored paper. Write a message or paste an interesting clipping, verse, or cartoon on each leaf. Paste the finished leaves in a scattered way, like falling autumn leaves, on a roll of narrow white shelf paper. Roll up the finished paper, tie with a ribbon, and send it to the sick friend. He will enjoy seeing and reading the "autumn leaf" messages.

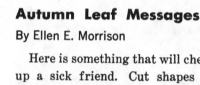

Loopy Creatures

By Lee Lindeman

A very different rabbit or chick can be made from heavy paper that has been cut into strips about 1 inch wide by about 10 inches long.

Make a large loop from one strip to form the body. Glue the ends together. A paper clip will hold them while the glue dries. Add a head from another slightly shorter strip. Fill the large loops with smaller ones as shown, gluing as you fill. These may be made from narrower strips if preferred. Add legs, wings, tail, and ears, cutting and creasing to the desired shape.

Glue the chick or rabbit to a base. Or you may want to tie a string to the top and hang it as a mobile.

You will have fun creating these loopy creatures.

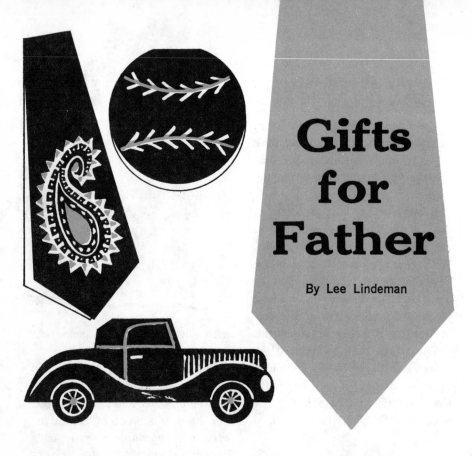

Gifts for Father

By Lee Lindeman

Special Cup for Father

Ask your mother if you may have a large plain coffee cup that she does not need. If she does not have a plain one for you, you can buy one at the dime store.

On a piece of paper draw a few designs for the coffee cup. Perhaps you would like to include your father's name in the design. Choose the best design, and carefully draw it on the cup. Then paint it, using heavy poster paint or a paint that is especially made for china.

When the paint is dry, coat the design with liquid plastic.

Brick Bookends

Attractive bookends can be created from old building bricks. Designs or very simple pictures can be painted on the large sides. Use poster paint. When the paint is dry, spray or brush on a coat of clear plastic or shellac.

Glue to the bottom of the bookends a piece of felt that has been cut to the exact size of the bottom surface. This will prevent scratching the table or shelf.

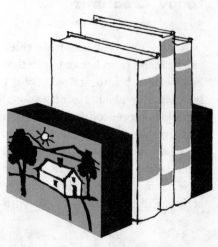

Batik Greeting Cards

This year make a new kind of greeting card for your father. The shape of this card and the way you create it are both new and different. The greeting card can be in the form of a baseball, a house, a tie, a car, or something else you think your dad would like.

Fold a heavy piece of paper in half. Draw the design shape of the card to include the fold. Using bright and light-colored wax crayons, draw the details and decorations. Press down heavily with the crayons. Do not cover the whole card with the crayon, but let much of the paper show.

Using a dark-colored poster paint, apply a thin coat evenly over the entire front of the card. The wax-crayon design will show through like magic.

When the card is dry, cut the folded card from the piece of heavy paper. The greeting card is now ready for your personal message to be printed inside.

Painted Ashtrays

A clear glass ashtray can be made beautiful by painting a design on the bottom of the ashtray. Here is a chance to use your imagination. Perhaps you will make an abstract design.

Use heavy poster paint and make your design very neat and colorful so that it will show nicely through the clear glass.

To make the design more permanent, spray or brush over the design with clear liquid plastic.

Case for Sunglasses

This case is made from felt and is very simple to make. Measure and cut a piece of paper that is 7 inches long and 3 inches wide. Round off the corners. This is to be the shape of the case.

Pin the paper shape to a double piece of felt. Carefully cut the felt around the paper pattern you have made. Remove the pins and the paper. You now should have two pieces of felt that are exactly the same size.

Sew the two pieces of felt together with colorful heavy thread or yarn. Leave one end of the case open so the glasses can be inserted.

Decorations cut from small pieces of felt can be added to the sunglasses case. They may be initials, stars, fish, birds, or any desired shape. Glue these designs carefully to the case.

Feather Pen

If you have a long feather from a duck, turkey, pheasant, partridge, or other large bird, you can easily use the feather to create an attractive feather pen.

You will need a new ball-point ink refill. You can buy one at a drugstore, variety store, or dime store. Place the ball-point refill at the lower end of the feather. Tape the feather and the refill together

Pop Art

On a 9-by-12-inch piece of drawing paper, print with crayon or felt marker the letters of your father's name. Make the letters so large that they bump the side of the paper or another line. You may make the letters upside down or at an angle, but do not cross over any line.

You have created many shapes. Now make lines within each shape. Then follow the outline of each letter to make an allover design.

Mount the finished design on a large piece of paper, leaving about an inch on all sides.

 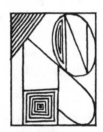

very tightly. This should be done very neatly and carefully.

Cut a piece of string about 2 feet long. Glue one end of it to the lower end of the pen, and wind the string tightly and evenly around the taped area until you have covered about 3 inches of the pen with string. Cut off any extra string. Glue the end of the string securely.

You may paint the string or leave it the natural color.

Egg Carton Pipe Rack

Use a molded-type egg carton. Cut from the carton a section with four cups. They should be in a row and not cut apart. Shape as illustrated, cutting only enough to make the section neat. The bowl of a pipe will fit into each cup.

Mount these pipe containers on a small piece of wood or fiberboard which will serve as the base. The board should be as long as the strip of egg cups, and twice as wide. Glue the bottom of the egg cups near one edge of the base.

You will also need a heavy piece of corrugated cardboard that is twice the size of the wood base. Score the cardboard down the center. Glue one half of it to the bottom side of the base. Bend up the other half on the scored line and glue it to the back of the pipe containers.

When the glue has dried, paint with poster paint or enamel. Decorate it any way you wish.

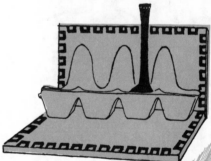

Let's Make These

Pencil Holder

By Katherine Corliss Bartow

Cut a strip of flexible corrugated cardboard across the grain, 3½ to 4 inches wide by 16 to 24 inches long. Roll up the cardboard and glue the end. Hold with rubber bands until dry.

For a man or boy, glue a part of an old travel map around the holder. Glue colored string or yarn around the top and bottom edges.

For a more feminine holder, paint it a pretty color. Some cardboard used for packing comes already colored. Decorate with a cutout flower or make your own. Finish top and bottom edges with glitter.

A taller holder could be made to hold knitting needles.

Spool Bouquets

By Ruth and Lois Dougherty

You will need an empty thread spool for each flowerpot, and construction paper, crayons, paints, and sturdy, thin wire for the flowers. Use the wire as is, or wind tightly with green crepe paper.

Use enamel or poster paint to cover the spool. Three or five lengths of wire, roughly three times as tall as the spool, make a nice bouquet.

The fun comes with making the flowers. Purple triangles, red squares, white squares with crayon markings, slipped onto a stem, look pretty. Use your imagination in fashioning a colorful bouquet.

When the flowers are finished, wind the wires together at the bottom and put into the spool hole.

These spool bouquets make appropriate gifts or party and tray favors.

Stick and Ink Painting

By Lee Lindeman

Find some twigs, small branches, or stiff dried pieces of straw. Even a toothpick or a pencil with a broken point could be used.

Dip the stick into colored or black ink, and paint a picture on smooth or rough paper. Use a different stick for each color. Experiment with different strokes so your picture will have an oriental effect.

Box Bookends

By Lee Lindeman

Find two small boxes that would be the right size for bookends. Fill with pebbles, small rocks, or stones. Replace the covers and tape the boxes shut, using gummed tape or strips of newspaper dipped in glue or paste.

Paint the boxes with tempera or poster paint.

Decorations can be painted on with poster or tempera paint. Or designs can be cut from colored paper and glued to the bookends.

For a permanent finish, spray or paint with clear lacquer.

Button Pictures and Cards

By Katherine Corliss Bartow

Select flat, white, two-hole buttons for these pictures. Backgrounds are cardboard or construction or drawing paper. For greeting cards, fold drawing paper cut to desired size.

Draw figures with ink, crayon, or colored pencil. Lay button head on figure. Mark eyes through holes. Remove button, and color eyes. Glue button back in place. Color a red mouth, pink cheeks, and brown or yellow hair.

Use scraps on hand to finish the pictures. For the samples illustrated, embroidery thread was used for jumping rope, wagon, and balloon strings, and construction paper or wallpaper for the skirt, wagon, and balloon. Button wheels were colored with a felt marker.

See if you can think of other pictures.

A Necklace

By Lee Lindeman

Find a branch about 2 feet long and an inch thick. Cut it into ½-inch discs. Smooth each one with fine sandpaper. On the edge of each make a groove with a file or knife. Repeat on the opposite edge.

Use a double piece of heavy string and tie around the disc. The string should fit into the grooves on each side. Tie a knot and place another disc between the strings. Repeat until the necklace is long enough to slip over your head or tie around your neck.

Put a small dab of glue over the string where it lies in the grooves in each disc. When the glue is dry, put a thin layer of colorless nail polish over each disc.

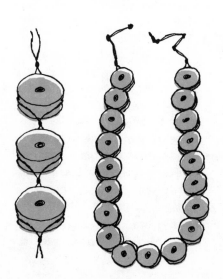

Fluffy Animal Portraits

By Lee Lindeman

Draw and color an interesting picture, with an animal drawn very large.

For the curly effect, cut thin strips of colored paper about ¼ inch wide and 2 inches long. Curl the strips on a pencil or with a scissors blade. Make smaller curls on a toothpick. Glue or paste the curls close together on the animal. Now you have a picture that looks good and feels good.

What about a curly poodle dog? Or a fuzzy lamb, a horse with a shaggy mane, a rabbit with a furry face?

Party Favors From Cardboard Tubes

By Deirdre B. Watkins

Cut cardboard tubes from wax paper or bathroom tissue to any desired length.

Cut fancy gift wrapping paper, crepe paper, or several thicknesses of tissue paper to go around the tube. Make this at least 5 or 6 inches longer than the tube. Wrap the tube and paste the seam. Tie one end with ribbon.

Fill with candy, balloons, or other small favors. Tie the other end. Fringe ends if desired.

The tubes may be decorated with stickers, pictures cut from magazines, artificial flowers, sequins, or glitter.

These cylinders may also be used for wrapping small gifts to be hung on the Christmas tree or pulled out of a Jack Horner pie.

Things To Make

Gold Candy Dish

By Katherine Corliss Bartow

Scour the printing from a plastic cottage cheese carton and lid.

Coffee grounds, thoroughly dried, are used to decorate. With a toothpick, dot white glue, a small area at a time, in the design desired. Sprinkle coffee grounds over the glue. Shake off excess.

Decorate the lid in the same way, leaving a small area in the center. In this space, glue an artificial flower.

With the lid on the carton, spray gold paint over the top and sides. When dry, turn upside down and spray the bottom.

These dishes, when filled with candy or cookies, make attractive gifts. They may also be used as powder or trinket boxes. The taller carton may be used as a vase.

Doll-face Mirror

By Katherine Corliss Bartow

Glue one end of a popsickle stick to the back of an old purse mirror. Decorate the stick with colored designs if desired.

Use a little cotton to pad the end of the stick. Then cover the entire back of the mirror with cream or pale-pink paper or felt for the face. If paper is used, apply two thicknesses.

Cut a 16-inch length of yarn for the doll's bangs. Spread glue on the forehead and loop the yarn back and forth. Cut six 13-inch strands of yarn. Tie them together about a half inch from one end. Divide into three parts, and braid to within a half inch of the other end. Tie. Glue the braid around the top and sides of the mirror, leaving the ends free about a quarter inch above knots. Tie a ribbon bow on each braid over the knot.

Glue on blue eyes and red mouth of felt. Make eyelashes with black pencil, and color cheeks pink.

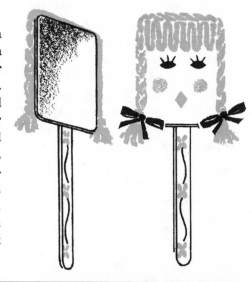

A Little Yellow Duck

By Luella Pierce

Use a yellow paper lunch bag about 5¾ by 11 inches. Fill this bag about halfway with shredded or crushed paper. Tie tightly with string. Spread out the top half of the bag. Draw eyes and lashes with black crayon.

Cut out a large bill and feet from orange construction paper. Staple the feet to bottom of the bag. Fold the bill to resemble a duck quacking. Glue in place about an inch below the eyes. Cut wings and tail from yellow construction paper. Staple the tail to the wings, and the wings to the body at the back on the bag creases.

If the duck is used as a favor and place card for a party, it could be filled with candies, peanuts in the shell, or other articles.

Peanut Shell Picture

By Phyllis Fanders

On a sheet of blue construction paper, paste grass cut from green paper. Place peanut shell halves to form flowers, butterflies, bugs, worms, snakes, birds, and the like. After deciding which shapes will be used for each object, and what color they should be, remove the shells and paint them with show card or water color paints. When dry, paste them onto the picture. Bits of green paper make stems and leaves for flowers. Pipe cleaners form the body and feelers of butterflies.

Gay Giant Bugs

By Lois and Ruth Dougherty

Use imagination to make your own fantastic bugs in addition to the ones shown. If you are a budding entomologist, interested in the study of insects, look in an illustrated dictionary or a book on insects to make real-looking ones. Insects are fascinating creatures.

To make the bugs, you will need corrugated cardboard, assorted colored pipe cleaners, fine wire from a hardware store or florist's green wire, poster paints, brush, and scissors.

Draw the outline of each bug on the cardboard, and cut out. Be certain the "pipes" of the corrugated cardboard go CROSSWISE on each body so the pipe-cleaner legs can be inserted.

The ladybird beetle shown is somewhat oval and about two inches long. This size uses pipe cleaners cut in half for legs. For larger bugs, one pipe cleaner will be needed for each leg. Put the pipe cleaner in one side of the body and out the other. When the legs are the same length, bend into position.

Now paint the bug an over-all color of your choice. The legs give something to hold onto. When dry, paint on designs. You might like to practice first on an outline of the bug, and then choose the best design.

Finish by inserting the wire antennae at the top of the head.

All insects have six legs. Spiders have eight, but they are correctly called arachnids, not insects. However, you might try making some spiders, too!

Basket

By Phyllis Fanders

This gay basket is made from a plastic shampoo bottle. With pencil, mark off the bottom third of the bottle, and a long strip up each side to form the handle. Cut out along the pencil lines. Punch a hole in the end of each strip and insert a ribbon. Tie together to form the handle.

Blowing Bubbles

By Maude E. Hallmer

Here is a way to make a special bubble mix that will make more beautiful, lasting bubbles.

Fill a quart jar two-thirds full of soap flakes. Add 1 teaspoon of sugar, and 4 teaspoons of glycerine. Fill the jar to within a half inch of the top with lukewarm water. For colored bubbles, add a few drops of cake coloring. Screw the lid on tight and shake the jar very hard.

To blow the bubbles, pour a little of the mixture into a saucer. Put the remaining mixture in the refrigerator to keep it for another time. However, when using the mixture, it will make better bubbles if it is room temperature, or even warmer.

Use an empty spool for a soap-bubble pipe. When you have a big bubble on the spool, swing the spool gently, and the bubble will fall to the floor. Let it fall on a woolen rug and the bubble will last a long time. Sometimes it can be made to dance by blowing gently on the rug near the bubble.

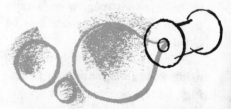

Flying Bugs
By Katherine Corliss Bartow

Use an ordinary wooden clothespin for the body. Attach fine wire to the clothespin for a hanger. Make eyes and mouth on the head of the clothespin with black crayon. Glue on pipe-cleaner antennas.

Cut four paper wings. Glue two together for each side. Draw on designs with colored pencil. Glue the wings to the sides of the clothespin. Add touches of glitter to wings and body.

These flying bugs may be hung in windows or doors or in the patio.

Bright Birds for Your Flowerpots
By Texie Hering

Each bird is made from two wooden ice-cream spoons glued together. Inserted between them is a small piece of Popsicle stick cut to beak shape, and a long Popsicle stick cut to a point at the end which goes into the flowerpot. In the illustration, each bird is shown with a different shaped beak.

Before inserting the beak and the stick, sandpaper the ends quite thin so the two body parts may be glued together firmly.

Paint the birds on both sides, using your imagination or following pictures you may have.

A Totem Pole
By Helen Mayfield

Use a cardboard tube from paper toweling or wax paper. Divide the tube into four equal parts with very light pencil lines around the roll. Mark a straight line in each section for the nose so the faces will be in a straight line. Draw eyes, nose, and mouth in each section. Draw the same faces on the back of the tube. Color the faces heavily with crayons, starting at the top and coloring downward so the colors won't smear. Make the eyes as large as you can, and outline with black. A coat of shellac or varnish will make the totem pole more durable.

Paper Portraits
By Florence Hodges

With paper strips imaginatively put together you can make interesting stand-out pictures.

On white construction paper or cardboard, sketch a face—serious, pretty, or comic.

Cut assorted colors of construction paper into strips about a half inch wide. Outline your pencil sketch with white glue. Stand the edges of the strips on the glue outline, bending or pinching the strips when necessary to follow the design. Curl strips of paper over a pencil to make hair. Fringe a wider piece and curl to make eyelashes. Combine colors to bring out the design.

Tomato Basket Fun

By Elizabeth Sheard

Save plastic tomato containers which come already cut out in fancy designs. Two ways of using them are described here, but you will easily come up with your own ideas.

Stand three containers on end and tie them together with white yarn. Use a fourth box as the base, placing in it a bar of plastic foam cut to fit. Arrange the three containers around the base, and tie them in place with yarn. Stick a bouquet of artificial flowers in the foam.

The other illustration requires five containers tied together around a circle of plastic foam, with flowers in the center. Attach a yarn hanger.

Potato Place Cards

By Dorothy R. Appleton

Place cards make seating arrangement at a party simple. Each boy or girl looks for his or her name and takes a chair. It is faster than pointing to where each individual is to sit, and with these unusual place markers, interest is aroused immediately.

Sweet or white potatoes are equally good for these markers. Choose fairly smooth ones, and scrub them well. Cut off one end so they will stand.

Features may be painted directly on the potato or may be drawn and colored on a sheet of paper, cut out, and glued on. Parsley is used for hair and attached with toothpicks or straight pins. Collars or caps are easily made from fluted paper cups.

Imagination will dream up many interesting and unusual ideas. Why not try a few before your next party?

Tube Town

By Lee Lindeman

Mailing tubes, and tubes from toilet tissue, paper towels, wax paper, and aluminum foil make wonderful buildings. Paint, paste, or cut out the details.

Use your imagination to design the window, doors, and signs for your buildings-in-the-round.

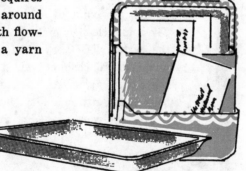

Letter Holder

By Lee Lindeman

This letter holder is to be hung inside the house near the front door. It can be used for mail that you want mailed, or for other members of the family to use. It is also handy in the kitchen for holding reminders, notes, and recipes.

Use two molded cardboard trays on which fruit is bought. One is used for the back and should not be cut. Cut the other tray into two pieces, one part half as large as the other. Glue the large piece to the second tray, and the smaller piece to the larger piece as shown.

Paint this holder with poster paint in any desired color. After the paint is dry, designs may be added with crayons, felt-tipped markers, or paint.

Egg Carton Animals

By June Rose Mobly

Gather together empty egg cartons, pipe cleaners, poster paints, and scissors. The egg cartons may be either the square kind or the oblong kind. With these simple materials, you can make a large group of animals. Use your imagination to see how many you can make.

Of the animals pictured here, the main body section of the cat, whale, duck, pig, bird, zebra, squirrel, octopus, and reindeer was made from two pieces of an egg carton lid which were fastened together with pieces of pipe cleaner run through holes. The holes can be made with a darning needle, the point of scissors, or a paper punch. The pipe cleaner ends are folded flat against the carton. The body section of the turtle, elephant, and dachshund was made from the lid of the whole carton. An egg cup was used for the body of the giraffe and the lion.

The legs were shaped with scissors at the bot-

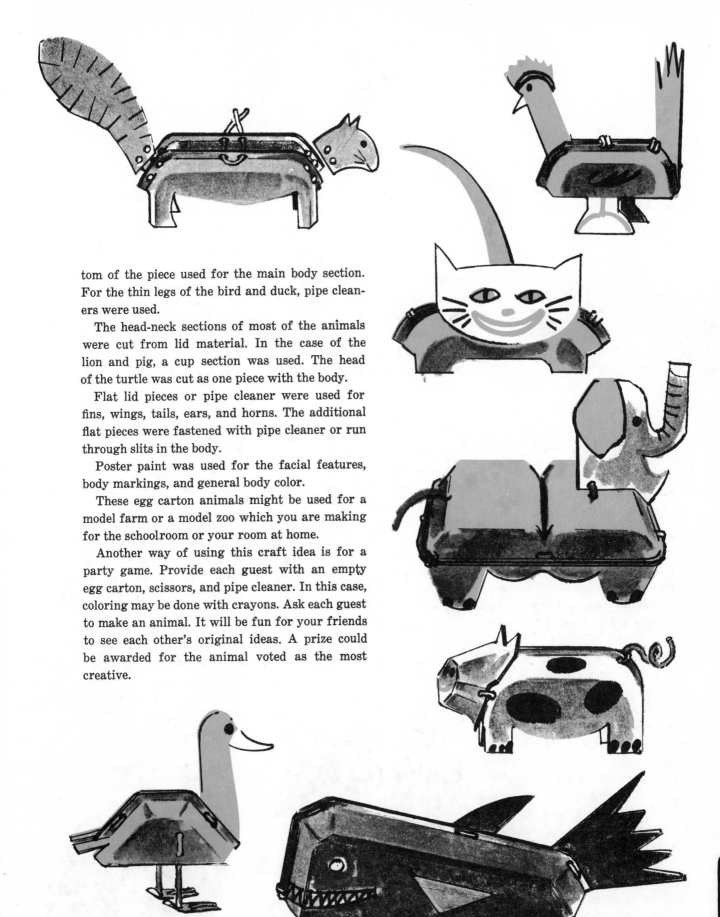

tom of the piece used for the main body section. For the thin legs of the bird and duck, pipe cleaners were used.

The head-neck sections of most of the animals were cut from lid material. In the case of the lion and pig, a cup section was used. The head of the turtle was cut as one piece with the body.

Flat lid pieces or pipe cleaner were used for fins, wings, tails, ears, and horns. The additional flat pieces were fastened with pipe cleaner or run through slits in the body.

Poster paint was used for the facial features, body markings, and general body color.

These egg carton animals might be used for a model farm or a model zoo which you are making for the schoolroom or your room at home.

Another way of using this craft idea is for a party game. Provide each guest with an empty egg carton, scissors, and pipe cleaner. In this case, coloring may be done with crayons. Ask each guest to make an animal. It will be fun for your friends to see each other's original ideas. A prize could be awarded for the animal voted as the most creative.

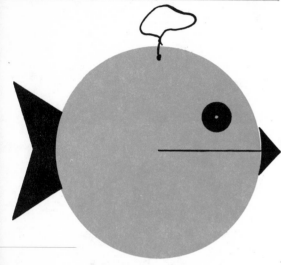

Circle Fish

By Frances M. Callahan

With a compass, draw two 4-inch circles on one color of construction paper. Cut them out. Make a cut from the outer edge to the compass hole in the center. Overlap the cut edges a half inch and glue in this position.

From another color of construction paper, cut a mouth and tail. Glue them to one of the circles as shown, with the mouth at the overlap seam, and the tail center exactly opposite the point of the mouth.

Glue the edges of the two circles together, matching the overlap seams. Add sequin eyes to each side of the fish. Attach a thread hanger.

Circle fish make interesting mobiles or window decoration, or may be hung from twigs of a leafless branch mounted in a container.

Willow Wisps   By Jean Freedle

These cute little furry animals are drawn around pussywillow catkins, and make clever greeting cards.

Use white paper 4½ by 6 inches. Fold it to 4½ by 3 inches. Glue one catkin for a head, and one for the body. Let them dry.

To make a kitten, a bunny, or a bear, draw in the background, their ears, tail, legs, and perhaps a few whiskers.

Plastic Perches

By Texie Hering

These may be used in potted plants or to decorate the table or to cling to mesh curtains. They are made from discarded plastic containers.

Draw and cut out a paper pattern. Trace around it on the plastic and cut out. Paint and decorate both sides as desired. Insert wire hairpins through small holes at the base of the body, twisting them together to make them firm. These are the "stems" to insert in the soil or the curtain.

Glue a colorful tie at the neck, using a strip of narrow ribbon with a knot in the center, or a small bow cut from paper or felt.

Using a toothpick dipped in vegetable coloring, carefully add eyes and a mouth to the face.

Print an appropriate greeting— for example, "Hope your birthday is purr-fect" or "I can't bear it when you're sick."

Paper Montage

By Ingeborg Smith

A cigar box or even an ordinary paper box, plain or printed, can be disguised as a gift box by using your imagination.

Cut colored pictures from old magazines or catalogues into oblongs, triangles, and wedge shapes, in sizes not over two or three inches long.

Begin by pasting shapes with the straight edges along the outer edges of the box, leaving a narrow border as shown. Then, working toward the center, cover the rest of the box, selecting pieces that will fit, or cutting them to fit. Leave about ⅛ inch between all pieces. Finish with a coat of shellac.

Fake a Snake By Candida Palmer

For the snake, choose an old sock with a good striped or zigzag design. The size of the snake will depend on the size of the sock.

Lay out the sock as flat and even as possible. The top of the sock will be the tail end.

Start cutting the sock, one side at a time, in the shape shown—narrow at the sock top, wider toward the toe. When cutting the second side, be sure that a good piece of the design will be included in the fabric.

Take about half or less of the cut-off portion, roll it into a ball between the hands, and tuck it into the toe end of the sock. This will be the head.

To form the snake, wrap the sock around the head very tightly, rolling edges in till they meet neatly on the underside of the snake. Continue rolling the sock into a tight roll, using pins to hold the edges together. Try to have the most colorful part of the sock showing on the snake's back. Sew the underside together with small stitches from head to tail.

Sew or glue on buttons, sequins, or felt for eyes. Make nostrils with marking pencil or paint. A narrow split tongue may be made from felt or plastic. If the sock is too plain, sew a bright piece of rickrack all the way down the back.

Other knitted fabrics such as old striped T-shirts also make good snakes.

Baking Cup Flower By Gladys Emerson

Cut slits in the rim of a paper baking cup, from edge to bottom, all the way around. Press out flat as shown.

Cut stem and leaves from green construction paper and a pot from any color desired.

Assemble the pieces on a 9-by- 12-inch sheet of white paper to form a flower in a pot. Fold the leaves in half and paste one half to the sheet, letting the other half stand out. Paste the flower center, curling the petal tips forward. Add a small yellow dot on the flower center.

Melt a Picture

By Lee Lindeman

Save little pieces of crayon that are too small to use. Shave off bits of the crayon with a knife. Place or sprinkle these small bits on a sheet of paper in a pleasing arrangement. Place another sheet of paper over the crayon pieces. On top of this, place a paper napkin or towel. With a warm—not hot—iron carefully rub over it.

Before the melted crayon cools, separate the papers. Keep the one that has the more interesting arrangement. Or you may want to keep both papers.

Add accents using chalk, paint, ink, or crayon.

Each melted picture is different. Experiment by brushing paint over the melted wax picture or dropping some tempera paint on parts of it.

Nutty Fun
By Texie Hering

Unshelled peanuts and almonds can be made into all kinds of things. This is fun to do any time, but makes an especially good party game.

Assemble some unshelled almonds and peanuts, ink, paint, glue, construction paper, crepe paper, and other odds and ends. Pick out odd-shaped peanuts that look like some kind of creature. Paint and decorate them accordingly. Combine the nuts into something larger like the clown and turtle shown. You will come up with some surprising and unusual results.

Make Your Own Stationery
By Marjorie R. Eichmann

Use plain note paper. Glue a large white two-hole button in the middle. With a little brush, very carefully paint the inside of the holes black for the eyes. Then paint two little shoulder lines on the paper, and some hair and buttons and a collar. With red nail polish, paint a little mouth.

Cut out a hat from colored felt. It can be any shape, but be sure it is a little wider than the button. Glue the hat onto the paper, with the bottom just covering the very top of the button head. Glue on a feather, with a sequin at the quill end.

This same idea can be used to decorate place cards, or tallies for Mother's card party.

Pictures
By Phyllis Fanders

For the background, paste a strip of green construction paper across the bottom of a sheet of blue paper.

Cut train cars and engine from colored paper. Paste to the background sheet. Add pop-bottle caps for wheels and puffs of cotton for smoke.

Paper Bag Puppets
By Rowena Cox

A paper bag puppet is easy to make and fun to play with. You can create any kind of puppet by just using your imagination in creating its face and clothes.

With the paper bag folded, cut away two V-shaped sections, as shown, to make a neck.

Unfold the bag. On the sides of the front section cut two armholes as shown.

Draw the face and costume. Add hair, if you like.

Tie a string or ribbon around the neck, leaving enough room to insert your three middle fingers into the head. Put your thumb and little finger into the armholes and make your puppet perform!

Create an Original Doll

By Ella L. Langenberg

It is always fun to discover what can be done with materials that are close at hand. You may have straw, pine needles, palm leaves, reed, or raffia. Pipe cleaners are always available. Whatever material you have may be made into something if you let your imagination work.

The little doll shown here was made with pipe cleaners. Use as many as you think will make a body for the doll. Tie them together at the neckline. Use another bunch for the arms. Divide the first bunch in half for front and back. Slip the arms in below the neck. With thread, tie the arms at the shoulders and around the body. Tie at the wrists and the waist.

The head is a ball of cotton. Make a hole at the bottom and slip the ends of the pipe cleaners into it. Stretch a piece of cloth or face tissue over it, and tie it around the neck. Add face features, using very little ink or paint. Glue on yarn for hair in any style you wish. From a square or triangle of pretty cloth, make a bonnet or babushka to cover the back of the head and any exposed threads.

Use brightly colored cloth for a skirt. This can be made by cutting a circular piece of cloth, then cutting a hole in the center for the waistline, and a slash from the outer edge to the center so the skirt can be fashioned into a wraparound skirt. Finish the waist with wrappings of yarn or a ribbon sash.

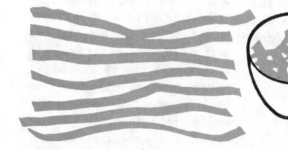

Pins From Paper

By Muriel Anderson

Cut several newspapers into strips about a half inch wide. Place them in a bowl of water and let them soak for a few seconds. Remove, and squeeze out the excess water. Tear into tiny pieces.

Mix flour and water thoroughly to make a smooth paste. Don't use too much water or the paste will be too thin. Place the pieces of paper in this paste to soak for a few seconds, and remove. Squeeze out excess.

Work this pulp like clay, molding it into the desired shape for the pin. There are many subjects to choose from—an animal, a storybook character, or perhaps the face of a friend. Be sure to work on a flat surface.

After the pin is shaped, apply a thin coat of the flour paste over the surface. Run a knife under the pin so it will not stick too tightly to the working surface. Allow the pin to dry. If placed in the sun, it will dry in a few days. An oven will hurry the drying process. Heat the oven, then turn it off. Then place the pin in the oven, but watch it carefully so it doesn't curl or burn.

When the pin is hard and dry, rub it with a fine-grained sandpaper for a smooth surface. Papier-mâché absorbs paint quickly, so give the pin two or three coats. Let one coat dry thoroughly before applying the next. When the last coat is dry, cut a narrow slot in the back, long enough and deep enough to insert a safety pin. Use a tiny pin that opens and closes easily. Use wood cement — sometimes called plastic wood — to hold the safety pin in place. Let this dry thoroughly. Then cover the papier-mâché pin with clear shellac. After twenty-four hours, give it a second coat of shellac. The pin should now have a smooth shiny surface.

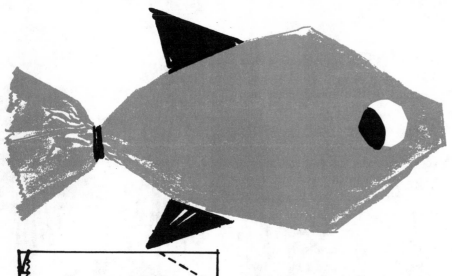

Paper Sack Fish

By Gladys Emerson

The size of the paper sack will determine the size of the fish. Fold the two bottom sides over to form a pointed nose, and paste.

Tear an old newspaper into small pieces. Wad and pack them into the sack to form the body of the fish. About two inches from the top end of the sack, tie a piece of string or use a rubber band. Fan out the top of the sack for the fish's tail.

Paint the fish with water colors or tempera. From construction paper, cut two triangular fins. Paste one at the top and one at the bottom of the fish's body. Cut and paste on two large round eyes. The fish may be hung with a string fastened to the top fin.

Nature Picture

By Marion Betz

Saw a 4- or 5-inch square from a wood shingle. (Larger or smaller squares may be used.) Sand the edges of the square, and paint it with two coats of tempera or poster paint—any color but green.

After the second coat is dry, glue on a spray of arborvitae (which has been pressed in a book). Arrange kernels of corn around it in flower shapes, until a pleasing arrangement is made. Then paste them in place. Put a heavy book over the completed picture, and leave it for at least an hour. Cover the entire picture with white shellac. Put a cloth hanger on the center back with a thumbtack.

Snowman Door Hanger

By Katherine Corliss Bartow

Scour the printing from six white plastic lids from cottage cheese or food containers. Use four lids to make the body. Cut off the rim of each, leaving a circle 3¾ inches in diameter which will be just outside the raised groove. This raised part will serve to give the snowman body a finished edge.

Cut the remaining two lids to 2⅞ inches in diameter for the head. Lay one head and two body circles in a row. Glue a narrow white ribbon down the center of the circles to connect them. Glue the remaining head and two body circles over them, covering the ribbon. Insert red ribbon hanger between the head circles. A red ribbon tab may be inserted at the bottom on which to sew bells, if desired.

Decorate both sides of the snowman. Glue two felt hats, back to back, on each side of the head. In the same way, glue on four red felt mittens, ten black felt buttons, four black felt eyes, two red felt noses, and two red felt mouths. Trim the hat and mittens with glitter. Dot glitter over the body for snow.

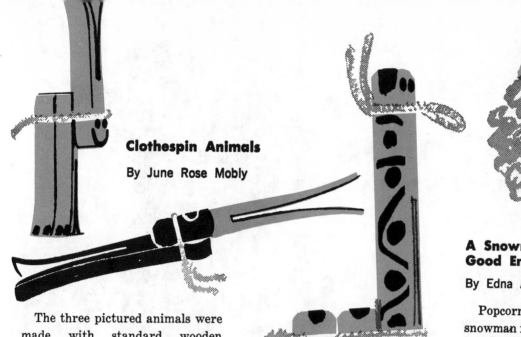

Clothespin Animals

By June Rose Mobly

The three pictured animals were made with standard wooden clothespins, pipe cleaners, and poster paint.

Mule

To fashion the body, tie together with pipe cleaner the heads of two clothespins, leaving a length of pipe cleaner for the tail. Attach a third clothespin which is upside down so that the prongs resemble long ears. Paint facial features on the head of the inverted clothespin and hooves on the prong tips of the other two.

Bird

The bird is made by attaching the heads of two clothespins together so that the prongs of one form the beak and the prongs of the other form the wings. The ends of the pipe cleaner are twisted to form the feet. Paint as desired.

Giraffe

The giraffe is formed by wrapping a single piece of pipe cleaner around the lower part of one clothespin and the heads of two others. Leave a length of pipe cleaner for the tail. Wedge a piece of cardboard between the two body clothespins. With another piece of pipe cleaner, form a nose and horns on the head of the raised clothespin. Paint spots and features.

Color Pyramids

By Ruth E. Whitnah

Build a tall tower of colored paper "bricks."

Cut out little strips of paper, as shown, in different colors and shades, from old magazines or catalogues.

Paste the largest strip at the bottom of a card or piece of heavy paper. Paste the next strip, in a different color, above the first one. Keep going in this way until the tower is finished.

A Snowman Good Enough To Eat

By Edna Alstrom

Popcorn balls make wonderful snowman favors. Your party guests will enjoy them more if they can make their own.

Give each child a popcorn ball, small black gumdrops or raisins for the eyes and mouth, and a big red gumdrop for the nose. Also furnish each one with toothpicks with which to fasten the candy features.

A big gumdrop topped by a smaller one will make a hat. Secure with a toothpick.

Have extra popcorn balls for eating, so the snowman favors can be carried home.

YEAR ROUND

Things To Do

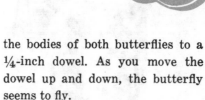

Flyaway Butterfly

By Gladys Emerson

Draw a butterfly on a piece of white paper and cut out. Paint designs on the wings with water colors, or color with crayons. Cut a second butterfly the same shape and size from colored construction paper. Place the construction-paper butterfly beneath the painted one, and fold the wings upward on each side of the body. Staple through the bodies of both butterflies to a ¼-inch dowel. As you move the dowel up and down, the butterfly seems to fly.

Designs and Pictures By Ruth Dougherty

On half a sheet of colored construction paper make a design or picture outline, drawing it lightly with pencil. Go over the lines with glue. Immediately sprinkle the glue with soap powder (or sand, coarse salt, or sugar), using fingers or a spoon. When completely dry, tilt the paper and lightly tap off the excess material onto another sheet of paper. Fill in any blank spots, and repeat the process if necessary.

Some designs are best left just this way. Others look well with each section crayoned or painted in with poster paint, using colors in combination or different shades of one color.

From scraps of colored paper, cut a house, barn, trees, boats, figures, vases, or whatever is needed to complete the picture. The powder is perfect for snow scenes. The dried powder may be colored with a light swish of paint for grass or sky.

The illustrations are examples of how you can create your own designs and pictures. They look well mounted on a larger sheet of a contrasting color.

Fishbowl Catchall Tray

By Texie Hering

Cut off the bottom of a plastic bleach bottle to make a shallow tray 1¼ inches deep. Mark the top edge with black paint. Then paint a row of fish all around the outside of the bowl with water ripples under them. In the inside bottom of the bowl make rows of ripples with fish at intervals half out of the water. Patterns are shown for the fish.

Paint each fish orange, leaving a small white spot for eye and nose. Then outline the eye with black paint, and make stripes on the fins and tail.

Popsicle-stick Airplane

By Donald Savage, Age 6

Take two Popsicle sticks and paste them together like the small letter t.

Take a third stick. Break it in half and rub both ends of one half against a stone to smooth the ends. Then take the other half and with a knife cut it short enough for the tail fin of the airplane. Paste these tailpieces to the body of the plane.

Plaster of Paris Picture Carving

By Lee Lindeman

Put a thin coating of vaseline inside a small cardboard box. Fill the box with mixed plaster of paris.

To mix the plaster, fill a bowl with water and carefully add the dry plaster of paris until it is as thick as melted ice cream. Quickly and carefully pour the plaster into the cardboard box.

Plan a picture or design for your plaster tile. Draw it lightly on the plaster. Carve the lines out with a pocketknife or linoleum carving tools. After you have finished carving, paint the picture or design with poster paints. Shellac or spray with a clear plastic if you like a shiny finish.

Box Town

By Lee Lindeman

With paint, paste, paper, and cellophane you can use a box to make any kind of building you desire. You might use a matchbox for a house chimney or an empty tissue roll for a factory chimney.

Use your imagination to build a whole town with stores, houses, churches, and factories.

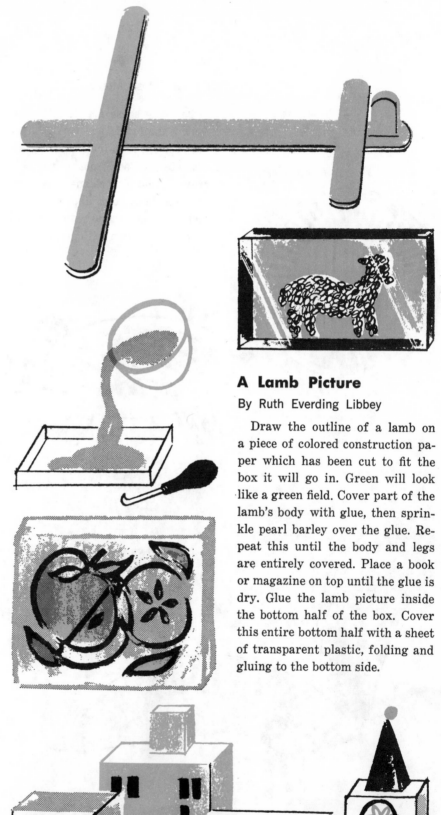

A Lamb Picture

By Ruth Everding Libbey

Draw the outline of a lamb on a piece of colored construction paper which has been cut to fit the box it will go in. Green will look like a green field. Cover part of the lamb's body with glue, then sprinkle pearl barley over the glue. Repeat this until the body and legs are entirely covered. Place a book or magazine on top until the glue is dry. Glue the lamb picture inside the bottom half of the box. Cover this entire bottom half with a sheet of transparent plastic, folding and gluing to the bottom side.

Things To Make From Paper Plates

By June Rose Mobly

To make these articles, the following materials are needed: paper plates of 6-inch and 9-inch diameter, scissors, poster paint or crayons, and pipe cleaners. Animal features, body color and markings, and car wheels and windows are painted or drawn with crayon. The various sections of each article are tied together with short pieces of pipe cleaner which are threaded through holes punched in the paper plates.

Bird in a Cage

Cut out and color a small bird. Cut bars in the flat center section of two small plates. Attach the bird to one end of a pipe cleaner and place the other end between the plates which are fastened face to face. Attach a pipe cleaner handle.

Turtle

From a small plate cut out a turtle. The center of the plate forms the shell. Along the ridged rim cut legs, head, and tail. Draw the shell design before coloring.

Octopus

Cut a large plate in half. Cut the halves into octopus shape, starting at the ridged edge with the head, and ending at the straight edge with the arms. Place the pieces face to face so each set of arms fans outward. Fasten together as shown.

Skunk

Cut a plate in half. Place the halves face to face and secure the curved rim with pipe cleaner. Cut along both straight edges to form legs and body; and along rim to form head and ears. For the tail, use two half-plates as for the body. Curve and feather the straight edges. Attach to the body.

Car

Cut away the straight edges to form wheels. Fasten the halves together, face to face, at the curved edges. Draw people in the car.

Caterpillar

Cut three 6-inch paper plates in half. Cut a half circle out of the center of each of the straight edges. Place the halves face to face and attach the curved edges with pieces of pipe cleaner. Cut a tail and head from another plate. Place between the body parts and fasten with pipe cleaner. Color as desired. Fasten all sections together with pipe cleaner.

Woodpecker

Fold a 6-inch paper plate in half. Cut into wing shapes, leaving them joined at the fold. From another folded plate cut a head, feet, and tail. Cut another plate in half for the body. Place face to face with the head, legs, and tail between. Fasten with pipe cleaner. Put the wings in a slit in the body. Glue or staple on a beak. Color as desired.

Cat

Cut a 9-inch paper plate in half. From the straight edges cut out a large half circle. Shape the front and back paws. Cut a tail from another plate. Color as desired. Place the halves face to face with the tail between. Attach with pipe cleaner. Cut out and color a head and neck from another plate. Place across the body. Fold the neck back and pinch it down on the body. Attach with pipe cleaner.

Baby Carriage

Use two plates, cutting away one-fourth from each as shown. From another plate cut two pieces shaped like phone receivers to be used for the springs and wheels. Fasten the matching pieces together, face to face. Then fasten the spring-wheel section to the carriage section. Add a pipe cleaner handle, and a baby cut from paper.

Blockless Block Prints

By Evelyn Minshull

Draw the design or picture on ordinary paper. Make the lines heavy. Turn it face down on a square or rectangle of heavy cardboard or corrugated paper from an old carton. Transfer the design to the cardboard by rubbing over the back of the paper with pencil or scissors handle. Retrace the lines.

Cover a small area of the design with glue or paste. On it, arrange rather heavy twine with a hard twist, following the line of the design. If the twine pulls away, hold it for a moment until it sticks. When the complete design is outlined, and filled in if desired, cover with a thin coating of paste and set aside to dry.

Daub tempera paint quickly to the twine design with a small piece of sponge, place it face down on construction paper with a pad of newspaper beneath, cover with a board, and stamp on it.

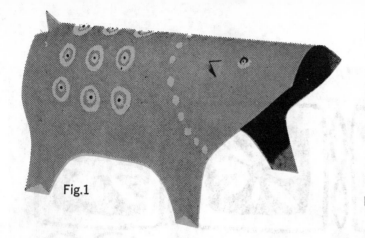

Fig.1

Fig.2

Fig.3
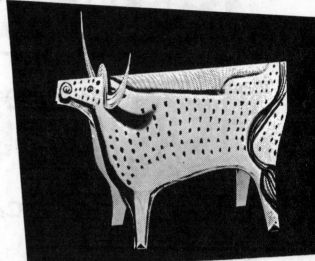

Animals From Paper

These animals are made from rectangles of construction paper or lightweight cardboard. Figures 2, 3, and 5 are creased at the top. Others are rounded without creasing as in Figures 1 and 4. Legs and sides are cut out, and the form is bent so that it will stand. In Figure 4 the paper is overlapped underneath to hold the form together. Additional parts, like the porcupine's quills, head shapes, horns, and tails, are cut out and attached or inserted in slits. Features, stripes, and spots can be done with ink or crayon.

Observing real animals will help to create better figures.

Adapted from "Creating With Paper" by Pauline Johnson, published by the University of Washington Press, Seattle, Washington.

Fig.4

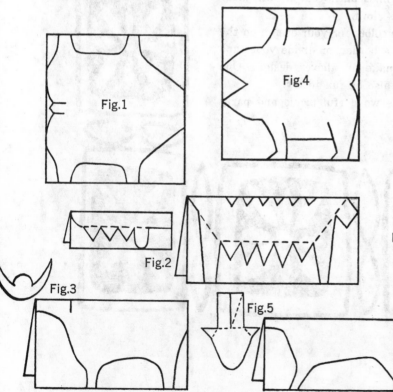

Fig.1

Fig.4

Fig.2

Fig.3

Fig.5

Fig.5

Tapa

Crushing Fun

By Lee Lindeman

What is tapa? Tapa is the bark of a kind of mulberry tree from which a cloth is made. The bark is pounded until it is very thin. Then the bark is soft and really looks and feels like cloth.

You can make a tapa cloth from brown wrapping paper. Start with a piece about the size of a place mat. Crush the paper with your hands. Open the paper, smooth it flat, and crush again. Repeat this many times until your brown paper tapa feels as soft as cloth.

Pick two or three colors for your design on the tapa cloth. Design a border, or divide your tapa into squares and make an allover design. One large design would also be fun to try.

Tapa cloths make wonderful picnic and party place mats.